D0969653

Five

i

This edition of **Five Women Writers of Costa Rica,** first in the series of anthologies by women writers, commemorates the FOURTH ANNIVERSARY of the ASOCIACION DE LITERATURA FEMENINA HISPANICA and of its journal, LETRAS FEMENINAS, which were created to promote publication and scholarly studies of literary works by women throughout the Hispanic and Luso-Brazilian cultures.

Victoria E. Urbano
President Founder and Director
Asociación de Literatura Femenina Hispánica

Five Women Writers
Of Costa Rica

Short stories by
Carmen NARANJO
Eunice ODIO
Yolanda OREAMUNO
Victoria URBANO
Rima VALLBONA

Victoria Urbano, Editor
Asociación de Literatura Femenina Hispánica
1978

iii

VICTORIA URBANO, Editor
Pat Hollis Smith, Assistant Editor

First edition printed by:
Lamar University Printing Department
Beaumont, Texas in the United States of America

*To all women writers who, in oblivion of
critics and publishers, unselfishly have kept
on creating their legacies for the world of
beautiful Letters.*

INDEX

ACKNOWLEDGMENTS

This anthology has been sponsored by the Asociación de Literatura Femenina Hispánica under the academic direction of its Founder, Dr. Victoria E. Urbano, with the collaboration of the following members:

Alicia Aldaya, Catherine G. Bellver, Elizabeth Espadas, Kathleen M. Glenn, Vivian Gruber, Mary Sue Listerman, Corina S. Mathieu, Martha Onan, Marie J. Panico, Katherine C. Richards, Pat Hollis Smith, Arney L. Strickland, Victoria E. Urbano, Rima Vallbona.

Gratitude is also expressed to:
Joan Burnett, reader
Eduardo C. Bejar, Roberto Olivera and Nuria Vallbona, translators
and to Lamar University professors: George De Schweinitz, Marilyn Georgas, Nora Leitch, Elizabeth Meeks, and Arney L. Strickland, English consultants.

INTRODUCTION

The five authors selected have contributed to enrich the contemporary literature of Costa Rica within the universal trend which distinguishes their own personal style. Their stories are interesting examples of art and imagination. They will help to acquaint the American reader with the feminine literature of Central America, so scarcely known for lack of commercial publicity, an evil which usually silences sensitive and talented writers from the Hispanic World.

The authors are introduced in alphabetical order:

Carmen Naranjo lives in Costa Rica. From 1974 to April 1976 she was Minister of Culture in the government of President Daniel Oduber. Due to this favorable political circumstance, she enjoyed a great deal of publicity and became better known as a novelist and short story writer. Most of her books have been published by government sponsored presses. However, she has not been studied, only reviewed in a very superficial manner.[1] In our commentaries about her creative philosophy, the readers will find guidelines to understand the meaning of her prose and her stylistical technique.

Eunice Odio and **Yolanda Oreamuno** are dead. They seem to have had parallel tragic lives. Outstanding writers, they lived the bohemian style of the expatriated intellectuals. Both were free, liberated, poor and brilliant. They shared identical experiences of men, sorrows, loneliness, and the addiction to writing. They lived in El Salvador, Guatemala and Mexico. These countries were for them like the Stations of the Cross, and Mexico was both Paradise and Calvary. There, they lived, agonized and died.

Eunice was beautiful. Her green eyes could only be surpassed by the beauty of her poetry. She was petite and full of passion like a Scarlet O'Hara, and like her, soon, everything, including her own life, was gone with the wind.

Yolanda Oreamuno had preceded Eunice in living, writing and dying. Her beauty was her most immediate source of tragedy. Her talent made her rebellious and marked her path to exodus. She was soon the victim of her own circumstances, and unable to escape her own unmerciful destiny she wrote wishing to open the "route of her evasion". But reality never let her go. She may be considered the first contemporary woman writer of importance in the literature of Costa Rica; however, it was in Guatemala where she first won recognition as a novelist and was awarded First Prize in the Guatemalan Contest of 1948 for her novel **La ruta de su evasión.**[2]

---

[1] The first extensive study on the poetry of Carmen Naranjo, by Victoria Urbano, is forthcoming in **KANINA** (Costa Rica's University journal).

[2] For complete information on this author consult: Urbano,: Victoria, **Una escritora costarricense: Yolanda Oreamuno,** Ediciones Castilla de Oro, Madrid, Spain, 1968.

Vallbona, Rima, **Yolanda Oreamuno**, Ediciones Ministerio de Cultura, San José, Costa Rica, 1972.

Victoria Urbano - what may I say about myself? - was like any other writer in Costa Rica, incredibly loyal to her art. When she was eighteen she packed her bags with a novel, many short stories, poems and one play, to go to San Francisco, California. In the Golden Gate City she wrote incessantly and then she went to Spain to write more and hasn't stopped writing since. In 1969, she entered an International Contest of short stories and with her book **Y era otra vez hoy** won the First International Prize for Literature "Leon Felipe". Thus she became the recipient of the highest International Award ever won by a Costa Rican writer in the literary field.[3] As a matter of fact, all the awards she has received are of international scope, from Spain, Argentina, Mexico and the United States.

Rima Vallbona is a dedicated writer who lives in Houston, Texas. She is not a frivolous author. Her main attempt is to portray life around her, but with dreams and poetry even though they are underlined with pessimism. Referring to her creative writing she confesses that "the irrational fact of having been born in order to die, is the basic conflict that generates her most essential topics." Arriving at her own conclusion that "happiness for the human race is almost impossible", she has written her most bitter and pessimistic pages. Her rebellion is expressed against the structures of the world, the injustice, and against life itself. In her own words, "when one has suffered hunger, cold, loneliness, humiliation, and has confronted extreme cruelty, it is impossible to stop belonging to the race of the crippled, the poor and the rejected. Rima states openly that loneliness is the keynote of her entire work. In her daily task of writing she has understood "how difficult it is to arrive at the heart of the eternal and of the true "and discouraged, she repeats that "writing is then a useless act, as almost all" and, with this conclusion in mind, she indicates that the most bitter aspect of her own existence is when she asks herself "if any one of the acts of life is truly worth the effort."

Rima shared with Alfonso Chase the Costa Rican Prize "Aquileo J. Echeverría" of 1968 for her novel **Noche en vela.** On August 26, 1977 she was one of the winners in the contest "Jorge Luis Borges" of short stories sponsored by the Fundación Givré in Buenos Aires, Argentina.

We are happy and grateful to present this collection of works by five women of Costa Rica who in their creative endeavors have shared one beautiful virtue in common: long years of loyalty to writing.

V.U.

----

[3] Chase, Alfonso, **Narrativa Contemporánea de Costa Rica,** Departamento de Publicaciones, Ministerio de Cultura, San José, Costa Rica, 1975, Vol. II, p. 117

Five Women Writers of Costa Rica

1

CARMEN NARANJO

CARMEN NARANJO

Born in Cartago, Costa Rica in 1931, she holds a Masters Degree in Liberal Arts from the University of Costa Rica.

She was Assistant Manager of Administration for the Social Security when in 1972 she was appointed Ambassadress for Costa Rica to Israel. In 1974 she was called back to become Minister of Culture of her country until 1976 when she resigned the post for personal reasons.

Her published works include **La canción de la ternura** (1964, poetry); **Misa a oscuras** (1965, poetry); **Los perros no ladraron** (1966, novel); **Camino al mediodía** (1968, novel); **Memorias de un hombre de palabra** (1968, novel); **Responso por el niño Juan Manuel** (1971, novel); **Hoy es un largo día** (1974, short stories); **Diario de una multitud** (1971, novel); and others.

She received the Costa Rican Prize "Aquileo J. Echeverría" in 1967 for **Los perros no ladraron,** and the "Premio Editorial Costa Rica" in 1974 for **Hoy es un largo día.**

Carmen Naranjo has distinguished herself as a serious and intelligent writer, deeply preoccupied with the vital problems of man and constantly searching for new ways of artistic expression.

THE FLOWERY TRICK

Translated by Corina Mathieu

Flowers and flowers and more flowers, he had to place them on the floor of the corridors, in the kitchen, in the bathroom, because the dining-room, the living room and the front hall could no longer hold the baskets, the flowerpots, the bouquets which were left without vases, the containers were all gone and the neighbors said thank you, thank you but they had enough with the eighteen arrangements that he had stuck them with. The knocking at the door, the please sign here and the here you are, is there a wedding? did not cease, and now they are knocking again but let them knock till they burst, there is no more room.

Before each of the first hundred bouquets he asked himself impatiently why, there was no reason; a stranger, a newcomer without any merit, a person that had never been awarded a simple welcome, except for the anonymous, impersonal, intensely cold ones of the roads and airports. He alleged the impossibility, that dissolved before the perfect coincidence of his name and address. But so many, so many flowers, not even possible for his funeral, his fingers were more than enough to count the few friends scattered throughout time and distance, none with means to buy flowers, nor the spirit to do it, even though they did not know of the hidden hatred, so intimate, against petals, fragances, corollas, the ostentatious beauty of the roses, gladioli, tulips, violets, the wild flowers, because he closed his eyes before the gardens, he escaped the comparisons of the fragrance and the grace of those inanimate things that cowardly soften the hard, disfigured and foul-smelling countenance found under all things.

To hell with the flowers and there they were, where there wasn't enough room nor were they wanted, despite that secret eagerness to express welcomes, heartiness, nothing more than a basis for moral support. He was choking, his asthma, the sneezes, the awareness that air was escaping him, they were stealing it from him, besides inundating him, pushing him out of his home with more haughtiness than the suspicions which he always encountered because his eyes were too open or he wasn't witty or he was never given enough time to retouch the photos of him taken by others. Never, that is the penalty, never the affirmation, neither the I nor the you emphasized. By itself it is already late, a lateness full of flowers that he doesn't understand and that perseverance in knocking at his door to saturate him with garbage and more garbage, because that's what they are after all, garbage, frivolous ornaments, indefinite messages, gays' language, symbols of cowardice, the pastime of pretentious hypocrites. Also a passport, because they are never cheap, they are always expensive, flowers aren't just given away, the wild ones are never sent, it's always the special ones and behind them goes the please accept me, the invoices for a favor, the keep me in mind.

Anger flushed the flowers and their colors made a wild demonstration of hues and fragrances, until they succeeded in reaching heights of the greatest aesthetic evidence with the natural spilling of a humid, undeniable, perfumed splendor, in line with the roundness that the springing forth of a perfect fruit acquires, the child, the nail, the bullet, the skeleton, and even more lovely because the withering will adopt a recoiling rhythm faced with the evident conclusion that there had been an expressive and generous beauty.

Invasion, that's what it was, a planned invasion to his ridiculous abode, entirely somebody else's or commonly rented, whatever it may be considered, because his space was something transparent that belonged to him in relationship with its not belonging to others, like an impossible sign to draw because its color hadn't been anticipated in the color range, or because everything was taken up and he was in the way as a complete being that wanted to find his place with his name and an inconcrete legate of half hatched thoughts that can't be written and communicated because they are incomplete, and that is his only legitimacy, his only identification of inconclusive permanence.

Maybe at the beginning surprise had surpassed his own confirmations, but now that there were so many and they continued knocking at the door, they were bothering him more and more, they were curtailing the little space he had, he had already solved the problem of time with some easiness: it was a matter of being born every day, fast with breakfast the lactation of bad memories, to do with the musculature of complete lasciviousness the noon orgy in order to abuse of an organization at the service of the glandular ceremony, then to approach the evening with that agony that gives the sensation of one's wings having been castrated for a flight that behind the illusion of the trip only had catastrophe as a goal, and then to slide into the night with the baggage of death, carrying an orphan Lord's Prayer and a shallow Hail Mary, in order to ream out the insomnia and to tell himself without any hope I am awake in a sleeping world facing the changing mood of the moon, and the traveling cemetery of the stars and the somnambulist road of rotund suns against the back of a poor man, with an inconsolable self-pity and a dreadful fear of encountering his poverty without any magic mirror that might smile when he smiles and cry when he cries.

But the flowers could be something worse, melted candies to kill the formula of cream and sugar and coca and vanilla, or vials with insufficient vitality, or packages with bows and ribbons over a noise of shattered crystals, or marijuana smoke that the others smoke happily, or consolation letanies before the closed doors with banquet echoes, or anonymous christs that exalt the vulgarity of suffering. Nevertheless, they were flowers, more flowers with their calm perfumes and their beautiful petals ready to symbolize everything that is false, everything that is eternally false, everything validly false.

4

When he realized the punishment, he raised a barricade in the street with roses and carnations at the vanguard, lilies of the valley and tulips at the flank and many daisies indicating the moving around of baskets, arrangements and bouquets with torn off gladioli and lilies. Not a flower remained in the house, all of them were outside in the middle of the street, together with the last deliveries made by sleepless messengers totally convinced that they had seen insanity flourishing.

Then he slept very placidly, like one of those characters from a fairy tale, where no one knows whether they brush their teeth, wear pajamas, sleep in a bed, turn to one side, count before falling asleep or fall asleep immediately because the verb is magic.

The next morning he received a decoration with three solar stars adorning a lost sunflower of figurative proportions, in the name of a grateful citizenhood for the indescribable effort of embellishing the street. Besides, a scroll signed by the governor, in recognition of his initiative, an order to have his picture taken from the bust up, smiling, that would be placed in the Town Hall, and an invitation to speak about flowers in the civic auditorium.

Oh! Flowers, flowers, blessed flowers, those landscapes' elves, that explosion of happiness, that generosity without replica of the earth, that love game for which I love you, I love you not!

When he received the bills with the evidence of his own orders, his own solicitations, his own requests, he smiled with the exactness of an opened rose. After many days he wilted, maybe he had depended too much on the splendor, that always ends up lasting a while almost a little while.

THE JOURNEY AND THE JOURNEYS

Translated by Marie J. Panico

Punctuality was his most authentic credential, an English trait with an Italian smile, like any other world war hybrid. The manager had granted him five minutes at 9:15 sharp.

He awakened at 6 and awakened his other I's, smiling, sure of himself, fearfully calm, at the same time sweaty and aware of a bitter taste in his mouth. He forced himself to forget dreams: from now on he would only have time for dreams on Sundays, besides, he never really knew if he dreamed them or if he invented them for himself so that he would feel imaginative, a creator of nightmares and of intuitions.

He was ready at 7 and began to think that he had gotten up too early. The problem was what to do now. He played his luck with the crossword puzzles in the newspapers. He would have a magnificent one if he could at least finish the first without having to consult the dictionary, but that damned river in India and that cursed son of Cain, even with an encyclopedia he couldn't fill the spaces. The second one could be perfect and change his luck, but – that's life – there was a Pakistani river, a Greek mountain, Magellan's famous ship – who he was and what he did – Cain's son.

Bah! Stupidities! He was too rational to believe in those things; besides he would take the precaution of putting his right foot forward when he left and put on his good luck tie.

When he arrived at the elevator door, at exactly 9 o'clock, he had already forged profound slots of time and thought. He mused about already attained triumphs and those the future would hold: an uninterrupted elevation to promotions. Who could have told him, the barefoot orphan boy, that he would be rubbing elbows with the elite?

It wasn't easy but he succeeded. He started first in school by asking for pity with patience, hard work and goodness. It didn't work. Then he demanded, became violent and alleged discrimination, oversight and indifference. He became the master of good example, of high grades, and of everyone's protection. Silence is a bastard trait in this world of screams and ultimatums. "The key is to make yourself heard, to know how to present your own case, to be your own firm, strong and unscrupulous defense attorney." High school was easy and the university the ideal place, as his word, there, was the word of his conscience.

He wasn't happy with just any old position; he needed something different, good and distinguishing and his questionable background, his membership in an outcast social class, his illegitimacy got it for him like magic. The Rector, with a smile of satisfaction and a friendly slap on the back, gave him his diploma. He liked neither the smile nor the slap, which constituted a kind of collective charity that had declared itself victorious. The Rector was

6

mistaken. Nobody was, by nature, genuine and he, the only real victor at that moment, would not accept boundaries. He came this far alone, screaming, demanding to tread the rails that others tread naturally.

Still standing in front of the elevator, with eight others, he pressed the button again. 9:02. The car was still on the seventh floor. After 15 seconds it came down to the sixth and stopped again. He had been wise in anticipating a possible delay, you never know what can happen when you leave your own domain. He searched in vain for his own interested and affable smile reflected in the green mosaic tiles, standard facade of walls which like to feel clean. His height was there, though, on the thirty something tile. Tall, the tallest of the nine of them, though it was senseless to include the two women and the little girl. The hand of the clock moved to 9:03, the elevator passed by the fifth and the fourth and stopped again on the third. Why the hell doesn't it get here? He thought of the security of using the stairs, but why be impatient? He would be sweaty and nervous and lacking the tranquility essential when speaking with a manager and finalizing the details of an agreement. He should neither project an aura of need nor that of an overanxious applicant. In an elegant interested way, he would first outline his ideas and then state his conditions. He would control the baton and the manager would be orchestrated to come forth with the exact note. People who seek something and reveal a preconceived notion of inferiority, of being in the presence of someone who is somehow superior, are so mistaken! He does not believe in hierarchy or in the phenomenon of supply and demand. In this world everything is a matter of influence, there are more than enough stupid, idiotic supplications of please, if you like, and thank God. The babble of introductions, of insincere preambles, of gratuitous gratitude is deplorable, deplorable, lamentable and useless. Today's world is a theatre in which only the concrete has any value, the I am, I want, I offer and I wait, I hope, I give and I receive. In this theatre it is the manager who must vociferously demand the recognition of others. "I am here because you are an intelligent, hard-working man and an excellent person, I am not here to ask, I am here to offer you. . ." This is the ideal basis for beginning a good interview, everything else will follow naturally.

The group pressed toward the door. The elevator now on the second floor, was finally moving toward the main floor and the impatient people hurried to lose time. They were so jammed in front of the door that those on the elevator couldn't get off. 9:04. He pulls himself away from the group and tries to get through. When the door opens, there is mass confusion between those getting off and those getting on. A frenzy of mad, useless gestures. If he could, and if the opportunity presented itself, he would make a superb speech on human stupidity, the umbilical cord which all men have in common. The group is in the elevator and anxious to go, but the operator doesn't close the door. Is she waiting for someone else or is she amusing herself by staring into the lobby with those aluminum walled eyes. Walls, like the inside of the elevator.

Chronological time of seconds and minutes means nothing to her. Maybe she measures it in terms of hours or maybe even half-days. There is no clearer indication of one's inner self than one's concept of time. The person who counts seconds is powerful, pugnacious, courageous and extraordinarily sensitive. The person who counts minutes is productive and a champion of action. Those who ignore chronological time and its components show dangerous signs of decadence. Those who hardly measure days, except in terms of meal hours, are simple ants devoid of ideals or ambitions. The poor things who conceive time in terms of weeks may as well be asleep. The ones who extend it to months are lifeless, insensitive sleepwalkers. The irrevocably dead and buried are the ones who awaken once a year, scrutinize the agonies of life and send greeting cards. These are really on the cemetery's shores and their tomb-houses are filled with out-of-date calendars and almanacs, their atrophied minds are empty, even of a consciousness or concept of themselves.

The elevator operator finally pushes the door button and, as it closes, she asks the passengers where they are going while her yawning fingers push the numbered buttons. For a moment the panel doesn't respond to the touch of her fingers and 9:05. By 9:06 it will be on the tenth floor if there aren't any complications. The elevator stops on the second floor and a man carrying two heavy boxes gets on. Capacity: twelve persons. On board: 11. The lights flicker between the second and third floors. What's wrong? The operator hears the **spontaneous question. "Something hasn't been working right since we started up but don't worry, it's nothing."** Oh, the innate contradictions of simple affirmatives and negatives! The door gets stuck on the third floor. The operator pounds the button with impatience and insistence. "Look, lady, it doesn't work, I'll leave you off on the fourth and you can walk down." We keep moving up toward the fourth floor but the elevator refuses to stop. The operator abruptly stands up and leans on the button numbered five with the force of her whole body. The elevator keeps on going up and the light goes out. Fear is everywhere. It finally stops but who knows if they're between the fifth and sixth or where? 9:0?, he would have arrived at 9:06. What colossal shit! Now he would arrive late for the appointment and would have to begin the interview with apologies. What damned lousy luck! Now he was really going to scream out his true feelings, first at the moronic operator and then at that gang of imbeciles who stupidly argued over who would be the first to be the last. But, not a voice, not a groan, not even the sound of heavy breathing. "What's happening?", his fear filled, almost hysterical voice cries out. No reply. "Isn't there anyone here?" Fear made his words tremble. And as quickly as he had said them, he reached out and his hands touched the cool, aluminum walls, with their panel of buttons, their closed doors, their total emptiness. "Am I alone?" This isn't possible. Not counting myself, there were 10 people here. Not even an instant had passed and no one got off, the man with the two boxes got on - on the second floor. The lady with the little girl, the other one in the pink dress, the old lady, the two men in shirt sleeves, the one with the boxes, the boy in the school uniform, the old man with the black portfolio, the operator, and I. This can't be. It just can't be. Maybe they're hiding? Where? On the floor, of course, on the floor.

Crouching down, he ran his hands over every corner of the floor. Nothing, no one, only footstep dust, a piece of paper, his own shoes, himself, alone. He screams out for help. "This can't be, it isn't logical, ten people don't disappear just like that." 9:07, he guesses, the darkness made it impossible for him to see his watch. He starts counting seconds and becomes confused after 43. "There must be a secret door. That's how they got out."

Again he touches the walls, the floor, the door, nothing, not even a slight crevice. "Why didn't I think of it before? Up there, on the ceiling, there's always an emergency exit up there." On tiptoe, his searching fingers reach and find the fan, corners of indirect light and nothing more, not a screen, not even the outline of a window. Everything tightly shut, everything closed, everything untouchable. "It must be one of those models where the ceiling has to be taken apart for repairs and maybe they took it apart to get up to the fifth floor and escaped from there. But how did they do it so quietly, without planning it first, without helping one another, without asking my help? It must be 9:09, maybe even later. I must be calm, think carefully and logically." He screamed out again, this time even more loudly, and kicked the walls and doors. An empty, sonorous silence, a silence of muted voices, a silence of afflicted breathing, a silence of solitudes, of solitude, of his own desolation. No one, nothing, except himself, his own pounding heart, his own afflicted breathing, his own cold, sweaty brow.

"This can't be happening to me; anyone else would lose his mind in this situation but not me. But I don't want to believe I'm dreaming either. I'm a believer in concrete things, in things I can feel, see, hear, touch – not in illusions. I know I saw and heard ten people, now I neither see them nor hear them, nevertheless, they could not have disappeared just like that, such things can't happen, physical spaces inhabit space and time which exist simultaneously with our own subjective existence. At this time there are a multitude of elevators operating and nothing strange is happening in them, they are going up and down, picking up and dropping off people, just because, no inspections, no passports, they are the least bureaucratic of servants but nevertheless, they failed me today, not only did they isolate me completely, but this damned thing is playing around with my imagination and my fears. However, this strange, nasty trick isn't going to conquer me." He screamed again, this time hoarsely. His throat dry, sweating, his chest pounding. He manipulated the emergency bell on the button panel. "9:11, it must be at least 9:11 and no logical excuse. Oxygen must be diminishing. This is some kind of trick, something planned by someone and I'm the victim, the innocent one, deluded by the happenings, unsuspecting, ready to give in because of my own stupid innocence. How incredibly naive." Since he now feels victimized, he is comparatively calm and realizes that his eyes have become accustomed to the darkness and that he is alone in the darkness, categorically alone, trapped, with his watch ticking away the seconds, the minutes, the useless time of actively passive annihilation. He screams again, the candorous cry of the jungle, of the snarled forest, of the sky, of caves, but he senses that his cries fall only upon his own ears which intensify the shrieks of his anxiety. And his eyes, by the need to find something, anything, discover a rare, repugnant animal-like movement on the floor. He doesn't have time to think about what it is.

The light goes on for a minute and the elevator moves indecisively forward and backward without really moving in any sense. He takes advantage of the moment of light to look at his watch. He can't determine exactly - 9 something - but again in darkness he guesses that the hand is below 9:15, maybe 9:17. "The manager and the appointment? They can go to hell! The important thing now is to get out of here, get out of the trap, analyze and understand later what has happened, know the why and the how of it all. Nobody understands at first, most get lost in words, poor solitary words, no one really understands their true essence. They say they don't hear and ask for repetition and still do not understand, they never understand what's happening, they ask but they don't understand, they don't really comprehend the answers, they end up not even asking, not understanding and continuing in their tranquil existences. I'll know what happened and why it happened. I shouldn't worry about it right now. I'll find the truth and sooner or later I'll avenge myself, I'll have revenge. I'm patient, I know how to triumph and to live." He screams out again, not a cry for help but a demand, an insult.

Almost as an unconscious gesture he loosens his tie, takes it off, puts it in his pocket and unbuttons his shirt. Something cold wraps itself around his feet. He thinks it is the tie and reaches down. Instead his hand touches a cold dribbling body that makes its way up his legs with a kind of natural meek mandate, with a terrifying silence. He gropes for its head, its beginning, but cannot find it. He shouts out desperately, he tries to walk but falls down. He is conscious of not being able to separate his feet, but he takes off his jacket and uses it as a weapon in the destruction of this thing that is weighing him down and is already crawling up his knees. It has no head, no beginning, no end. He complains, but the only pain he feels is an affliction of his own anxiety. The light goes on for a moment, more quickly than a blink, hardly giving him time to recognize his own face, his horrified face, his staring eyes devoid of any expression except that of dense, dull, concrete and absolute fear. The twisted mouth, the clenched teeth, the jaws in strong strokes of unnecessary strengths. Lines of muscles and steam-like sweat on open skin, red stains and pores of purple scars. "No, that's not me, this is impossible, my youthful, fresh face. This is some game to drive me crazy. I can't stand the poverty, the oblivion, the sensation of marginal existence, the self-vision of impotence and the distant certainty of unimportance. I won't let them defeat me, this mirror game and the sensation of being tied up. They can crucify me but I will be resurrected, I will be resurrected. After this interminably long road of sacrifices, no one can defeat me, no one. I have known how to master the nerve-racking scale upwards. I am a piano capable of producing harmonious melodies. I'll climb up to executive committees and to directors' positions. This manager and lots of other managers will call me hundreds of times, they will consult me, adulate and flatter me, they will unremittingly recognize my intelligence, they will admire me in spite of their enmity and only in silence will they dare to remember my bastardly origin, my beginnings of misery and abandoned displacement."

He screams again, the cry is long and weak. This strange, cold, sinuous thing enveloping him has already reached his thighs and his grasping, groping hands still cannot find its head, its beginning or stop this thing's murderously oppressive movement. "Is this death? Is this death?" The idea crosses his mind in images which follow his morning activities, his wait for the elevator, his journey companions, his journey, the disappointment of the appointment with the manager. The fleeting unity in the instant of the happening, the others already gone, and him, alone, with his agony, with the awareness of death covering his body in sweat. He smiles to himself, these things only go in the minds of the tormented, those who believe in God and who, like good lawyers, already have plans for repentence at the final, universal judgment, the good and the bad; as if these were not concepts invented by the lords of leisure. He smiles to himself, a self-concept of security and independence is reborn, he is dreaming, simply dreaming, dreaming that he is dreaming, with eyes closed, because there's no one who can save himself from autosadism, he is dreaming that he is having nightmares and he stops to think about them, analyzing them in detail, he is not one of those who loses consciousness and drifts into the drunkenness of narcissism vitiated by alcohol, by drugs or by delusions of egoistic importance. Someone who is agonizing doesn't smile to himself and he is smiling to himself; if he were agonizing he wouldn't be able to smile; the tormented can't smile; they suffocate themselves in their search for air and are as dissonant as ineffective machines. No, nothing really serious is happening to him; it can't happen; he's never been ill and this sense of isolation is just a strange quirk. "A hallucination, that's it." The words penetrate slowly, even as he is saying them, and his anguish asks the meaning of hallucination.

"Hallucination. . .hallucination. . ." That strange thing keeps moving upward, his legs, his stomach. . .it's suffocating him. He cannot find his hands, his arms are useless. "Have my arms and hands been vanquished, are they bound and worthless? Hallucination. . .?" He acknowledges that he has never drunk a great deal, nor experimented with drugs nor been possessed by such strange sensations. Only reality and this vital constant effort to convert it to something favorable for him, for his growth, his development, his prosperity.

And what is more hallucinatory than reality? Perhaps he is sick of realities which are transformed or should be transformed into better realities.

An excruciating, pitiless pressure constricts his ribs. And when he can't stand it any longer, when he cries helplessly, when he feels that he is vomiting blood because they have him by the throat and are choking him, when he thinks about his life, and defines his whole existence as a total waste, he feels the floor tremble and he moves as cautiously as if he were taking his first step.

A sure, sonorous voice: "Your floor sir, the Managerial floor."

INVENTORY OF A RECLUSE

Translated by Mary Sue Listerman

the man stopped at a corner because he wanted to wait and perhaps he didn't stop entirely but rather leaned against the wind using the hump which surged from his own back when he wanted to rest himself

it is hard to say with any certainty what he was waiting for because he was waiting for himself and this takes a lot of effort to understand if one thinks about the fact that one is one and one always has one's self but the truth is that it's not this way and at times one has to wait for oneself

neither it is possible to explain clearly why he was waiting for himself since in order to do so one must know how to get up without a reason to walk out of habit to dress oneself unwillingly and to be completely bored and also to remember that not always is one himself who truly arrives at being himself except in a few moments of life.

there he was waiting for himself and then it seemed to him the right moment to contemplate those who were passing by and to meditate on their lives not really meditating but rather imagining or in other words distracting his waiting in order to give it a meaning or an exercise.

first he saw a blonde woman walking alone rapidly and he thought that he was thinking about his lunch menu but he almost didn't arrive at this thought for then he saw a very well dressed man who was lighting a cigarette and at this moment a vehicle sprung up suddenly.

inside the vehicle he saw a little girl with a very long neck who was playing with one hand out of the window and who became a little frightened on seeing his nudity but he didn't have time to notice any details because two men drew near to his corner.

these men were expressing loudly some political commentaries mixed with the account was the speck he had in one eye blurring his vision hurting him and also bothering him because since morning he had poked in it and hadn't found anything.

in the conversation it was said De Gaulle was a fool poor France but thinking it over perhaps Johnson may be worse and all the Russians worthless and worse are the Chinese and this eye which hurts and doesn't let me see clearly and thusly until they went away and the man thought he had heard them from within a dream from which he couldn't wake up entirely but it wasn't like that at all because he was on a corner waiting for himself.

a bus inundated him with fumes and then he believed it would be very easy to be run over and he saw himself in the middle of the street while the people through the window were shouting but he didn't want to see his blood nor feel the blow of the collision because he felt sorry for himself and couldn't tolerate this image.

and he felt afterward the sole of his foot itching him in a sort of tickling which demanded to be scratched immediately and he began to scratch himself slowly understanding suddenly that force is an idea and an idea a fire that bursts in thousands of stars.

when he stopped scratching himself mentally there crossed before his eyes the image of Johnson in such a strange way that he remained elaborating it like a face in a chair and in the face was growing the nose he made an effort to give him a body and the body that he achieved was a dwarfed and deformed trunk.

in his efforts to create Johnson's body he became furious because he had to give a body to him who had one and according with the time change between both their countries Johnson should be already sleeping or at least he was probably seated at his desk drawing soldiers and cannons.

upon imagining this last thought he said to himself that he was unjust with poor Johnson and then he saw him drawing cows on the blotter of his desk some little fat cows that were giving milk even through their ears the picture was so funny to him that he decided to make another one like it at the first opportunity.

he realized that by seeing these images he had missed a crowd that was crossing the street and was disappearing in the crossroads of the corner and their way of disappearing made him think that the eye or rather the range of the eye was the mark of existence.

he asked himself which would be the blind's mark of existence and then he understood that the eye has thousands of visions and in addition we have interior eyes which see memories and foreshadowings.

he felt very pleased at having perceived all this and he stopped at a white house which he hadn't seen before how strange because many times he had stopped on the same corner and on innumerable occasions he had passed by the street.

a white house so mysterious where he imagined that he would be able to live one day and he saw it mentally and even went in because at that moment he needed to urinate with a sort of pressing desire which changed to pain and which disappeared when he came out of the house and decided not to live in it.

in an instant someone greeted him from a car with a smile he had never seen before and when he was deciding to answer he realized that next to him there was a very beautiful woman who was smiling at the fellow in the car and waving good-by with her hand.

he imagined quickly a love story he wished to make her happy but something came up to make it clandestine and mysterious and while these thoughts were forming he contemplated the woman who walked in front of him.

she was old very wrinkled caked with make-up and he became frightened by her hips when she passed by very closely because he imagined them to be eruption covered masses of gelatine and because she destroyed the love story he had contrived in a vague way.

he thought that upon passing by his side the woman had smiled like a prostitute but perhaps she was smiling still from the memory of the man that passed by in the car and she was not one of those people who suddenly changed their expression as it happens with many who talk in the street and upon continuing their walk already have another face since they use different ones when they are talking or greeting someone.

he felt moved by the woman who kept on smiling because she had met an acquaintance or a lover and he saw her again when she was moving away and was already near the corner in which she would disappear and he found her beautiful again.

he wanted to know what time it was and he decided to find out from the first person who should pass near him and he met a dog sniffing his shoes and the dog seemed to tell him that it was about nine thirty.

but the dog kept on insisting not on the time but rather on sniffing him and he became afraid that the dog might confuse him with a post and this fear forced him to move and to chase it away with schhhs but the dog instead of being frightened and running away began to wag its tail.

he understood that the animal was looking for a master and then he felt that someone had found him and that he was on the point of not having to wait anymore for himself.

as always happens when one finds oneself with oneself our man on the corner felt a great nostalgia which could become a mournfulness if the dog hadn't begun to lick his hands.

or that could be changed into the beginning of a tiredness if he suddenly had not become aware of the fact that when one waits for oneself and finds oneself one begins the wait for something else.

what could he wait for?

without even stating this question to himself the answers surged but these weren't concrete either because the man felt the necessity of leaving the corner and began to walk followed by the dog which was trying to adjust to his steps and entangling itself in his legs.

the man disappeared from my window upon submerging himself in the other corner as if it were a curtain where people enter never to come out again just as in the moment in which they were still present.

nevertheless he didn't disappear suddenly because I continued seeing him walking and then halt at a window to caress the dog and to scratch again mentally the sole of his foot and to think that the little old woman who had crossed the street next to him needed to wait for herself on some other corner.

and when he had already disappeared completely from my thought I was left observing the round mirror of my room and in it a little bright hornet that was twirling around and around as if it was seeing itself and couldn't believe that it was he because when faced with the illusion of finding himself with one like himself he was looking for a means of communication.

this little hornet was so similar to the man on the corner that I felt like seeing the site of his wait again but all things have their time and their space which never repeat themselves again.

there was no corner in front of my window but rather a brick wall washed by the rain with strange figures and neither was there a round mirror inside the room because all of that had existed only a moment earlier when the eye blinked tired of retaining images.

The Creative Philosophy of Carmen Naranjo

by *Victoria Urbano*

In Carmen Naranjo's works we discover a series of dual symbols that revolve around her essential topics. The "I", protagonist of human existence, needs to find the magic thread to weave a tunic of eternity to protect itself from dreadful nothingness.

Death's inexplicable mystery and doubt constitute man's vital problem. For that reason, like a magician, the poet tries to find in his inspiration the drug to help him through his temporal transit. His inebriation becomes a chant to give itself to others as in a ceremony of light. Such is the religious-like inspiration that flows from Carmen Naranjo's poetry. For her, the personal voice is that interior light which each one has to conquer in order to defeat silence and death. The direct generators of her essential topics which appear in all of her works are: the deep human nostalgia for time's fugacity; the struggle to conquer pessimism and the inertia that takes hold of man before irremediable death; the anguish and oppression contemporary man experiences before the empty mechanization and speed that consumes him; the promulgation of a free voice, symbol of individual authenticity, in open struggle against slaving mediocrity, cruelty, indifference and disaffection of today's world. Her desire to find or regain that voice through faith and constance, makes her works to be anything but pessimistic.

Her novels reveal many points which reflect her own personal emotion and some very personal ideas. Thus, in almost all her books we find a repetition of images which first appeared like intuitive synthesis in her poetry. For this reason her narrative and short stories are better understood after reading her poems.

Her most fundamental and recurrent concepts are:

Time seen as the hunting for moments with a feeling of acute nostalgia because "that which is gone never begins again in any future time."

Today's automatism enslaves man in "a repeated type of life which is no LIFE". The individual, conscious of his own littleness tries desperately to live and work not knowing why nor how he does it. He becomes like a thermometer of private agonies looking for his place, time, size, reflection and self memory, and his life becomes an endless hour same as the one before.

The triviality of daily life makes the individual life like a story already told.

In order to break this monotony it is necessary to destroy with a brusque movement every paralysis to be able to reach authentic self-fulfillment. Instead of crying, man must bring forth his chant and without stopping, he must keep on assisted by faith which is the best but weakest element of human essence.

17

Together with faith, man must have dreams, because in the act of dreaming he finds himself free.

The words as symbols of voice or self authenticity, function almost like a protagonist in Carmen Naranjo's writings, because it represents man in open struggle against the agony of temporal existence, and against the negative elements that oppress him.

Love becomes for this writer "the sowing where we plant time, voice, seed and our own desire of growing endlessly."

In all these concepts or ideas recurrent in her works we find the writer's poetic philosophy which may be summarized by saying that man needs to create from mind, heart and body to save himself from being defeated by NOTHINGNESS.

Commentary to "The Flowery Trick" of Carmen Naranjo

by *Corina Mathieu*

Carmen Naranjo's "El truco florido" [The Flowery Trick] is a fine example of contemporary Latin American short fiction. Leaving aside regional considerations, traditionally a must in Latin American literature, and obviously ascribing to the latest prose techniques, the author has created a story in which the protagonist and his circumstance reach universal dimensions. There is a touch of magic realism in this surrealistic account where the protagonist is suddenly confronted with an invasion of floral arrangements apparently sent by an anonymous source. At first the bizarre incident appears too preposterous to consider seriously but slowly, as the story develops, the revelation of the protagonist's thoughts enlightens the reader. The ingenious "truco" is the attempt of a lonely human being to break the monotony of a drab existence and the barrier that separates him from his fellow men.

The story's structure respects basic tenants of the genre such as the mounting of tension and suspense, in this case created by the revelation of the protagonist's trend of thought through a narrator and an anticlimactic conclusion which adds the final touch of surprise.

Stylistically, the author's evident inclination for linguistic innovation is not always successful. In several cases the choice of unusual metaphors together with that of verb and adjectives in an unlikely context detract from the prose; they create unnecessary difficulty in the comprehension of the text while at the same time interrupting the smooth flow of the narrative.

All in all, "El truco florido" is an interesting story that reveals Miss Naranjo's undeniable creative talent and includes her in the evergrowing number of promising Latin American writers.

2

EUNICE ODIO

EUNICE ODIO
1922 - 1974

Born in San José, Costa Rica in 1922, she lived in different countries of Central America, Cuba, the United States and Mexico, where she died in 1974 under tragic circumstances.

After residing in Guatemala for several years she became a citizen of that country in 1948. But in 1972 she changed again to become a citizen of Mexico.

Eunice lacked a university career but she had numerous intellectual friends with whom she practiced the beautiful art of conversation and exchange of ideas.

Out of necessity, she became a self-made journalist writing miscellaneous articles for a small pittance.

She first won recognition as a poet in 1948 in Guatemala where she was awarded first prize for poetry with her book **Los elementos terrestres.**

Her other outstanding books of poems are: **Zona en territorio del alba** (1953), and **El tránsito de fuego** (1958).

ONCE THERE WAS A MAN

Translated by Elizabeth Espadas

Once there was a man who will be. . .Even I know that that isn't right. The correct thing would have been to say that once there was a man who was. . . He touched his head once more. Again he refused to look at himself in the small mirror that he used to shave himself when he couldn't avoid it. Once there was a man. . . What's certain is that now I don't have time to think about why I keep on thinking about this. And the truth is that, in light of the circumstances, and that (but what circumstances?) I am ignorant, it doesn't matter that "there was a man that **will be**. . ." He said that when he asked me for a match, but I called it "flame" as if I weren't from here. . .And from where, then?. . .A man that will be what? Why can't I remember the word, what the man was going to be?

Pedro didn't know if what obsessed him more was the word that was impossible to bring to mind or the man that said it. He didn't dare ask himself. What was strange about that man he had never seen before?. . . Tall, with blond hair that was brilliant (as if of gold). One sees that kind of physical type, both in foreigners and natives of the country, quite often. He didn't notice anything special about his accent. Only that. . .His words sounded as if they were distant and they came slowly, as if each one lasted centuries or seconds and that centuries and seconds were the same thing. . .But it's just that there are days that we **hear visions**. The man talked like everyone else. Perhaps the only strange thing about him was his eyes. To Pedro it seemed that they shed a phosphorescent light like the sea, when it is transparent and the sun shines on it. But that perhaps was due solely to the fact that his own eyes weren't working too well. . .The rims itched and they watered; any reflection, even just daylight, dazzled him. He couldn't admit to himself that down was growing inside his eyes.

A stormy gust of wind filtered in from someplace, raised up the ashes and cigarette butts from the small dish placed on the drawer that served as a night stand; it blew from the matchbook; it inflated the shirt hung on a nail; it resounded, shuddering; it seemed to run through the two poor rooms and go out as quickly as it had entered.

Another unpleasant surprise for these days! Hadn't he covered up all the cracks with boards and Resistall 5000, foreseeing the windstorms of approaching autumn?

After all, it is early. I have time to look for the place where it entered. It wasn't even daylight yet. He turned on the electric light and began to work. First he investigated his room, wherever he had covered a crack before and wherever he had not done it. Everything was in order: door, cracks, small window. Everything was closed up just about as tight as a drum.

In the other room the dishes handled by Emilia were already clanking together. Agueda kept on sleeping, under the pretext that she "washed up for others". And what must she do with the money from "washing for others"? Pedro would really like to know. Not for any real reason. . .Simple curiosity.

He searched, board by board, joint by joint. Nothing. Emilia was going to put the water to boil.

"Move from there for a minute so I can look."

"Look for what?"

"For the place where the wind came in."

"What wind"

"What do you mean, what wind? It almost blew the house down and you still ask! Women, when they aren't all upset, they're like sleepwalkers. Why can't they ever be like everyone else?"

Emilia looked at him with swollen, still sleep-filled eyes, surprised; but she didn't dare ask anything further.

"I didn't notice," she said, drawing away from the stove.

Nothing. There wasn't anything anywhere. How could that be? He spent quite a bit of his scarce funds to avoid the cold of a year ago and something turned out badly. May God have mercy! When one is poor, everything gets twisted up, especially life's path!

Before leaving, he recommended, "Do me a favor and look for it."

"Look for what?"

"Heavens! Well what do you think I've been looking for? The entrance of the wind!"

Later in the bus, that strange sensation of being divided into various parts and not knowing in how many began to plague him again. Except for his head, which he knew was divided in two parts by a middle line that forks (what in the world is a **middle line that forks**? For days phrases and words whose meaning he didn't know had been popping into his mind); and very large completely round and shining. Shining. . .Now he knew. . .Shining! He was horrified. The pit of his stomach curled up like a live oyster that had been sprinkled with lemon. He drew his neck down into his body, trying hard to hide that head that he couldn't recognize as his own but that nevertheless continued on top of his shoulders.

The gentleman seated in the row in front raised his eyes, looked at him an instant with indifference and continued reading the newspaper.

He didn't notice or he is a vain, nearsighted fellow that doesn't use glasses Or I don't have a shiny head. . .That's it. . .It's not shiny. Why hadn't he dared to look at himself in the mirror this of all times? Perhaps because. . .yes it was because of that, because Emilia hadn't looked at him in any special way as she would have if she had noticed that his head was shiny, round divided. . .But that didn't mean anything because Emilia was stupid and never saw anything. She was so stupid, that sometimes she believed that she was really his sister, as she said she was, just the same as Agueda, since the great catastrophe that destroyed the village and the children, forcing them to flee down the roads until arriving in Mexico, a long time ago. He knew that she wasn't, but he never said anything. What for? Two pretended sisters are better than none.

His head was rigid and shiny and his body had turned into unequal parts, different from the ordinary ones. He knew he wouldn't see the doctor.

The first thing he would do upon returning home would be to look at himself. . .

That must be stopped. . .Yes. . . That's what I've been saying. What in heaven's name is happening? It doesn't matter what has happened or is happening (What has happened or is happening?). . .The only important thing is to get to work and hope for luck (hope that people will throw out a lot of glass and dirty, torn papers, good for nothing). I am nothing since they are good for me. Thirty cents per kilo of waste paper, minus what the scale robs me of.

Pedro got off at the corner nearest his destination. He soon reached it, three blocks from there, where Neva and Lerma streets meet, whose residents pay him a small monthly fee for throwing their garbage in the collection truck each day.

While waiting for the vehicle to arrive, Pedro spreads out on the ground on one side of the road his big piece of jute and on it throws the contents of the garbage cans that he picks up from the doorways. Then he separates from the rest of the trash any glass and papers, all dirty, broken, and foul-smelling.

That day he began work as usual, separating some things from others: papers, here; clear glass, closer over here; colored glass (which sells better) over there.

It was Monday and he was surprised not to remember what he had done on Sunday, but it didn't bother him. He already had enough problems not to have to add to them worrying a bit about last Sunday. He continued sorting glass from the potato peelings, remains of rotting meat and newspapers; rotten carrots from glass; glass from grubs with beans.

Don Joaquin passed in his grey overalls, apron and gloves. Those bothersome gloves used by the "official" employees of the garbage truck struck Pedro as funny. The "independents" like him handle garbage "bare". A question of custom. . .Well, the use of gloves must be also.

Pedro got progressively filthier and filthier. He remembered with perfect clarity. Last Sunday was yesterday. On the corner, the man with the "flame" (who without a doubt meant to say match), in the middle of the great windstorm that had arisen, just like this one now, lit the cigarette cupping the left hand around it to protect it and said. . .He realized that **yesterday** was a meaningless word.

The great wind pounded the garbage and Pedro's face, blowing away the papers that the sticky slime hadn't made dense and heavy. A bad day! With the wind like it was, the best he could get today would be twenty kilos. At thirty cents a kilo, that would be six **pesos**. Just tell me what one can do with six **pesos**, with the cost of living so high and a head so. . .! He broke into a run into the wind that seemed like a squall and the sky was blue. He ran desperately after a handful of torn newspapers that were in flight. Pedro ran two meters and was blown back one from the force of the hurricane-strength wind; he was staggering and straightened himself up again so as not to fall. The wind raised him up from the ground a few centimeters and put him down again, still standing, where it had blown him.

He thought he heard Turcios saying "Look how well Pedro dances. How well!" He didn't think about it twice because he knew already that Turcios always made fun of all those that were less fortunate than he; but he ceased his persecution, perceiving its futility. When he returned to the piles he had made, he saw that the bulk of the paper had gone with the wind, while he had been chasing the handful. Why does one do such desperate and silly things?

He sat down on the edge of the sidewalk dejected. His head felt so big! And so completely round!

He had no desire to continue his work. He saw a bone button. He took it and put it in his pocket. Bone buttons and shell buttons he always took home where he deposited them in a shoebox. Around Christmas he sold all that he had accumulated. They were almost like a little treasure.

There was another button. He grew interested. . .There could be more. . .There were more. . .He searched anxiously in the miniature pigsty. Seven buttons! As he stretched out his hand to take the seventh, he saw that, for the hundredth time, a great piece of skin had fallen off him. . .

He began to walk mechanically. He reached the corner where he always took the bus to go home, but he didn't wait for it as he usually did.

He opened the door. It was very late. He made very little noise and fell asleep the best he could.

II

Pedro put on the pants that had always been large for him. It was impossible not to notice that today they were much too large, larger than ever. Just as if they were other pants. . .Or an item of apparel inadequate to cover him. . .Or as if he were another person. And yet they were the same pants as always and he was the very same person, either Pedro or whatever he might be. Isn't that true, Pedro? Yes, very true (What in the world is a **nervation**?) There was the big patch he looked at every morning in the world (but that didn't obsess him). He also thought he noticed that the shine of the pants (that didn't obsess him either) that had disappeared a long time ago beneath the layers of filth, now reappeared multiplied; no longer did they shine, they glittered. How quickly time flies when it comes to poor people's clothing!

Pedro was accustomed to "everything. . ." But the truth was that, especially lately, there had been (he was just about to say there will be and he was startled) things that. . .

Upon putting on a sort of vest (he called it a **vest** because the sleeves were of a different material, and evidently, without knowing the whys nor wherefores, had belonged to an unknown suit coat and everybody overlooked them), he felt something inside his arms.

He always got dressed in the darkness of the early morning hours. Now he turned on the light. He took off the "vest" and touched his left arm with his right hand and vice versa. He couldn't feel anything special by touch. He was going to put on the clothes again when he noticed that the fingers of both hands were light blue, sky blue. . . Upon closer observation he saw that the dust -- even finer than the most delicate aniline -- was coming from his arms.

He couldn't remember having handled any trash of that color. He tried to recall. No, there wasn't even anything similar to it. . . Although the truth is that yesterday he didn't feel good and he didn't know what was the matter with him. It could have been. . . He remembered that last night when he arrived he hadn't washed his hands and arms as he always did.

He went out to the patio, directing himself to the small basin that served for everything: sink, laundry tub, at times, bathtub. He lathered up and rinsed himself off furiously. He saw with pleasure that the dust disappeared. He returned to his room, he put on the vest and again felt something on his arms. It wasn't weakness; no, it wasn't that. Neither was it pain, although it resembled pain. Cramps? No. A confusion of the senses? No, although there was a little bit of that, too. . . Help me, oh my God! How can one be perturbed in the arms?

He looked at the clock. It was five minutes 'til six o'clock in the morning. Or. . .A shaken up heart. . .Man, of course! One can have a shaken up heart. Without looking any further, I myself. . .That. . .Well. . . Then one can be perturbed in the arms.

He didn't forge any illusions that his problem was solved, but it was close to six-thirty and he didn't have time to find out what it was that he felt in his arms and even less, why. He told himself he would see the doctor.

Emilia called to him that breakfast was ready. He hesitated. Should he go in the dining room or not? If he went out without doing it, perhaps she would think it strange and be suspicious. . . And perhaps. . . He went in.

On the table the watered-down coffee was steaming. Beside the cup, fried tortillas with **picadillo**.

"They're really good. I made them so you would eat. You haven't eaten anything to speak of for days. You're skinny, poor little Pedro. You're swimming in your pants, they're so big. You need some others."

Pedro shuddered right down to the bone. She had noticed. She knew. What did she know? What not even he knew? Had she noticed that he was tremendously thin? Anyone can see that -- he thought, calming himself. And if she had seen other things? Who knows what others see and keep to themselves? But Emilia didn't see anything because she was dumb. . . Dumb but good. He tried to eat in order to show his gratefulness for her kindness. He forced himself to take the tortilla. Even before doing it he knew it would be impossible to eat a bite. He put it down again on the plate.

"What's the matter with you, poor little Pedro? What hurts you?" she asked in a shy, broken voice.

"Why does she ask so many questions?" he thought. A surge of anger rushed through him as violently as fleetingly. He saw the untouched food and contained himself, saying: "Nothing, sis. Nothing hurts me. Don't worry."

Sister, little sister. . .He has said the word for the first time. Something happened or something broke down inside him. He got up and went out, feeling his arms.

In the bus that sensation grew stronger. No, it wasn't a sensation but an indefinable feeling. He moved his arms and shoulders up, down, up, down. An older man, with a red winter scarf around his neck looked at him with reproachful eyes, just as his teacher had looked at him ages ago. He remained still, feeling something impossible, thinking with all of his strength.

Suddenly, like a flashing image, a visible, inevitable word came to him: laughter. That was it, yes! His arms were laughing without shaking. They were laughing like he had heard that the blessed laughed: smiling. Contrary to the pants legs, which seemed to have stretched, the "vest" sleeves (that Pedro didn't suspect of not being such a thing because Pedro never suspected anything) seemed to have shrunk. Pedro believed that he noticed that they were changing color, too. How quickly time flies when it comes to poor people's clothes and they don't even realize it! he repeated.

He had spoken aloud. The man with the winter scarf looked at him reproachfully again, and nevertheless, with a certain kindliness in the depths of his eyes, something sweet whose fleetingness was endlessly repeated, like the sweetness of his teacher in his eyes and speech. . . Brother Gabriel was coming down the hill with him behind.

"Go home, Pedro!"

"Didn't you tell me that the Master called Peter? And you, my master, are sending me away?"

"You should be called more appropriately Angel and you should be one. That's all right, sit down and let's rest up from the descent, since later we'll have to climb up again."

Brother Gabriel put the books on the grass, spread out a large handkerchief and made himself comfortable at the side of the path. He took out another handkerchief and mopped off the sweat.

Pedro's eyes were fixed on a strange book that, on the outside, said incomprehensible things.

"It's in Latin, son, and don't touch it with dirty hands!"

"What does it say?"

"It talks about the angelic choirs."

"And what else does it say?"

Brother Gabriel opened the volume, read to himself a moment, two, ten. Pedro felt as if his teacher were quiet forever. Unable to contain himself, he asked the same question again.

"It says everlasting things."

"And what are everlasting things?"

Brother Gabriel lifted his eyes and Pedro also lifted his. The former said. "Do you see the heavens? They will not perish. Do you see that it is full of light? Light is also immortal and will live forever, it will travel never ceasing and never lessening. It is a form of God. You can't touch it but it is here everywhere. In these and other books you will learn about what doesn't perish. They are all beautiful and are worthy of keeping as we keep the holy days."

"Are these days that we keep?"

'Yes, my son. The same as we keep the oldest memories; the same as the Celtic coins that are somewhere, the same as the world, kept under seven keys and a Single Eye."

Pedro stuttered, licked his lips and pushed aside a lock of reddish hair. Then a torrent of questions came flooding out: "Father, what are the oldest memories, the Celtic coins that are someplace, the Single Eye, the. . .?"

"The seven keys are fire, air, water, earth and three other substances that will be revealed in their time. The rest I will explain to you another day. Now we must go to eat in order to return to the school. Come on, let's go."

"Father, just tell me where the days are kept."

"Some inside others. Come on, let's get going. It's late. . ."

Later, little by little, Brother Gabriel explained to him about the Celtic coins, the oldest memories, the Single Eye and many other things that "there are and there aren't in books," as he used to say.

Pedro looked again searching for the fleetingly sweet and reproachful glance but it was no longer there. At what time did he leave? How did he leave, if the bus hadn't stopped a single time? Since I began to remember the oldest memories until now, have they passed the place where I have to get off? Afraid, he looked out the window. They hadn't passed it. He realized that they hadn't because of the newspaper stand. After doing it for ten years, the route was very familiar to him. That seemed like too much to him.

"Didn't the gentleman in the seat ahead of me get off already?," he asked his neighbor.

"Which one do you mean?"

"One that was over there with a red scarf."

"The truth is I didn't notice. . .I didn't see any gentleman with a red scarf. There was no one. . . Well, I mean that one is distracted thinking about anything that comes into his mind and doesn't pay attention. I don't know. Was he something to you?"

"Yes," said Pedro in order to say something; "he is someone I hadn't seen for a long, long time. . .

And I didn't recognize him until much later."

"It happens like that," his companion on the trip said consolingly. They fell silent.

He got off at his usual stop. Rosa Luna greeted him with a certain indecisiveness, like he was a stranger. What was the matter with Rosa today? She said "hello" to him as if she had said something she didn't know anything about. How strange she was acting! Anyway. . .

He made an effort to work with diligence. Today there was so much glass and papers of different colors than he had ever seen before so that spurred him on.

As he always did before working, he bared his arms. Again they were covered with that very fine impalpable blue dust. He lowered his sleeves again quickly, ashamed and feeling that an inscrutable burden was hanging over him. Oh my God, I am alone in the world, have compassion on me!

As usually happened when he implored to God, now again he felt that the darkness was not total. Yesterday was a bad day. Today will be good. . . As Brother Gabriel used to say, all of them, good and bad, are our days and we ought not back away from any of them. . .

Why was he now remembering Brother Gabriel time after time?. . .Well, today especially could be explained. The man that looked at him like his teacher had done had gone away; or rather, he had disappeared like his teacher had when Pedro was nine years old. Perhaps just before the catastrophe that threw them out. . .Or with the catastrophe. He had never been able to unravel that and other knotty problems that he had all tied together in his head.

A feeling of nostalgia and oppression invaded him, while with his swollen fingers and hands as fragile as the rest of his frame, he sorted oceans of papers, colored glass and waste into piles, getting it all over him.

He began to place in a little sack that he always brought for that purpose a small portion of the colored glass that he didn't sell when it was as plentiful as it was today. Instead he took these and deposited them at home. They then formed a sort of stockpile in order to have a source of savings for unexpected emergencies which are never lacking.

He tied the mouth of the sack with hemp to go to store it as he always did until the end of the work day, at Neva 16. He couldn't lift it from the ground. It weighed more than if it had contained lead. He again tried to lift it and again he failed. Curiosity led him to take a piece of glass and put it in his hand. It weighed as much as a marble slab. Sometimes one can't lift something from the ground. . . But one is capable of holding it if someone else puts it on his back. . . And one can take it with both hands. He motioned to Juan, but the latter pretended not to notice or really didn't see him. . . Today is Tuesday. . . It's Phil's turn to come and I don't see him. . .so he can help me get the sack on my back. . . It doesn't matter. I wouldn't be able to cart the rest anywhere anyhow. Do things weigh more? Or do I weigh less? There was only one possible answer: he had lost weight and become debilitated and useless.

The sun was scorching in the cloudless summer sky. Pedro's blood thickened and smoldered. He felt cold and on fire. . . And the strong, hot wind was coming in his eyes, his mouth, his heart. He curled up in a small corner of the doorway where he had been working. The feeling of oppression returned. No, it wasn't that he "felt oppressed." He **was oppressed**. He could feel and see the link that oppressed him and separated him from the world. He saw don Joaquín, Juan, Rosa Luna and the rest of his companions, but rarefied; it was as if a pale, fine smoke had interposed itself between them and him; a smoky, fine, hard air.

He looked up the street. In some doorways, "his" garbage cans were still full, promising a good day's wage. . .At least thirty **pesos.**

He got up off the ground like one who gets up with the backbone not with his feet, feeling that his joints were weak and his bones dissolved, or just about to dissolve. . . He couldn't remain totally upright. I look like a poorly made pot-hook. . . I want a smoke. . . Can't even smoke. . . He tried to raise his hand to his shirt pocket where he kept his cigarettes. . . It was as if his hand were tied to a short rubber band that didn't stretch far enough. He forgot about the cigarette. He took a very short step, as limited as the movement of his hand.

He walked or rather he dragged himself a little bit at a time, like ants or. . .He didn't dare name them. . .

A man helped him onto the bus. He tried to thank him but was voiceless; he was aware only of a great feeling of repose. The man took a seat next to him and lit up a cigarette, with something that to Pedro looked like a huge blaze of fire. As he did it, he looked at Pedro from behind the flame. . . Through the fog that had enveloped his mind and body entirely, through the water that the glare caused in his eyes, Pedro thought he recognized that man; something about him was strangely familiar. Perhaps he was an acquaintance. . . Maybe even a friend. Perhaps – since he couldn't thank him – he at least ought to say to him "How are you? How have things been for you? How glad I am to see you!" or any other of the niceties one says to show that he is courteous. He couldn't articulate a single word. It was his tongue, that wouldn't obey him. He leaned his head back, resting it against the seat. . . It was his tongue. With it he touched his formless palate, which seemed to be filled with fine, voracious thorns. . .

He stopped thinking, even though he knew he should think about so many things. . .The immobility of his neighbor and the awareness of a great repose invaded him like a flood of enigmatic noises. He couldn't even think how long it would take him to reach his bed from the corner bus stop. First it was the awareness of the great repose. Then, it was the great repose without awareness.

III

He couldn't and didn't even try to undress to get in bed. Everything that covered him was too stuck to his body and was lukewarm and caressing. He didn't sleep. He rested, falling into a trance, in a fall upwards as if he had never been born or never had awakened.

The great solar river made him desire nudity. The weakness had abandoned him. Now he moved brusquely, violently. His suit tore at the back. He left it there. The house was silent. He went out just before the break of dawn. Nothing tied him, everything was gone except the wind. He ran in the morning air, fillng his lungs. He didn't wait for the bus. He didn't need it. He was swifter than the busses and more agile than children (he ran across one and compared himself).

He arrived much, much before the others: Rosa Luna, Juan, don Joaquín, Turcios, Rafaela, "Old Lady" Lupe. . . Before the garbage in the doorways. Before. There was nothing to do. For the first time, there was nothing to do.

He walked down the Promenade. He began to look around. He saw that he had never ever looked at anything. He made himself comfortable there, on the English grass, damp from the evening dew. He felt the pleasure of the strong, fresh dampness that was a witness to the forthcoming day; of the ray of sun that was moving; of the belltower that rang among the wild bees, from their perfect noise. The joy of having a lot of space for himself possessed him; the thrill of looking at all space and having it all for himself. He drank it all in. It didn't pass.

A distant, almost inaudible voice brought him back to the meadow. It was Agueda's. With a warm body and refreshed soul, he got up.

He went toward the small group. As he was approaching, he noticed that he was hearing their voices, not at a distance, in space, but at months of distance, with a temporal ear. In the group was the man of the "flame".

Pedro was so close. . .And they seemed so far away!

Agueda made a gesture, as if brushing away a fly from her cheek.

"Celastrina Argiolus," said the man of the "flame".

"What did you say?" asked Agueda and continued without waiting for a reply. "Last night he didn't come to sleep. If he were a person given to dissolute habits, nothing would surprise us; but he is modest, conscientious, humble and respectful. Isn't that true, Emilia?"

"Very true."

Don Joaquín threw a glance at his companions. They indicated agreement with their eyes. The old man stuttered:

"The thing is that we haven't seen Pedro since Saturday. We were already getting worried and were planning to go and ask you. . ."

"But he came," affirmed Emilia. But he went to work Monday and **Tuesday. I made him breakfast. . .And I made it for him Monday and Tuesday morning, as usual. It was last night that we didn't hear him come in to sleep."**

"We haven't seen Pedro since Saturday, we haven't seen him. . ." they all repeated like a refrain.

"Where are you going now?" inquired Juan.

"To keep on looking for him everywhere."

"Well, where must I be?" Pedro asked himself and he said to himself: "I have to help look for me and find me. Perhaps I ought to go up. . . From up there one can see better."

He went up to the top branch of a full-grown poplar. It delighted him to ascend so easily, but he didn't see anything of himself.

He got down and went to the foot of a laurel tree of incalculable age. Having reached the top of the poplar without effort spurred him on. He visually measured the great distance that remained between him and the top of the laurel tree. . . If only I could reach it. . . God! Help me to go!

He began to scale the tree, walking on the bark. Then he left the bark and began the real ascension. He was ascending with a crystaline heart, and unfurled, feverish body and freed lungs. Halfway up, he lowered his eyes and saw the Earth. He stopped a second. From the corner the man of the flame was looking at him. Around the man of the flame. Around the man of the flame were whirling leaves, making a sacred ring.

He comprehended, then, the vigilant wind, penetrating and possessing in its domain. He looked at himself. He saw that his feet had disappeared; his cells were leaning, shining in another direction. And he understood.

He was fatigued when he arrived at the crown of the tree, at the last laurel leaf. He felt the productive fatigue felt when one uses muscles long inactive. He raised up vertically his Celastrine wings of the summer.

And he stretched out.

He was the color of God and he was lying down. A sleeping butterfly.

THE TRACE OF THE BUTTERFLY

Translated by Catherine G. Bellver

"Theoretically it is possible," Hans said, moving across the room strangely. There was a strong gurgle. Rafael looked at the glass tube shaped like an upside down umbrella and connected to other bubbling glass objects.

Hans tightened the belt of his immaculate tunic. He went to the laboratory; he regulated the valve of the steam, which was escaping in small quantities then went over to a corner illuminated by a light that seemed to have no source. He opened the small door of the wall cabinet; he took out a glass bottle and served two glasses of a violet liquid.

"Your black elixir," mumbled Hans with the tone of a believer in prayer, and he extended his hand with the glass to the painter.

Instead of taking it, Rafael stood up and looked intensely at the liquid that Hans offered him and that, exposed to light, took on a dark olive tone. He brought his eyes up close to the surface of the full glass wrapped in undulant mercurial silver flames which flew, as if impalpable yet visible, in dimensions greater than their sphere of action. His eyes moved involuntarily from the waves of the flaming mercury to the hands holding the glass. He felt dizzy when he saw that the hand was animated inside by the same gaseous, undulant flame of mercury. . .Or was everything an illusion? Wasn't the mercury burning in the cells of that hand? Unwillingly he raised his eyes and looked at Hans! He saw a feverishness much more intense than usual. And also. . .Or was this another illusion? . . .The desire to give an answer. But Rafael never asked anything. He avidly took the glass, while the cold bonfire of its surface grew and the flames escaped, took on a spiral form, and dissolved upon contact with the air.

Although he had been a witness many times to this thing called **inhuman landscape**, he never ceased to feel that he was in a strange, undescribable state. And in spite of the innumerable times he had received that unique gift, he had never before been that close to the mercurial waves; the master's hand went beyond its corporeal limits. In whose presence, in what presence was he? How many times had he asked himself the same question?

At the bottom of the glass a spark of silver persisted. After a few seconds it went out. Then he took his first sip. He recognized once again the taste that delighted all his cells, making it seem as if they were turned into bodies with gustatory organs linked together in one sensorial attraction. He savored the liquid little by little and he became intoxicated, with an intoxication that had nothing to do with wine although it did give what could be called supreme energy of the conscience. He was not alone with Hans. Along with him his cells, which he felt as contents and not containers, were becoming intoxicated in this grand and lucid delirium of the conscience. All of a sudden it ceased, as suddenly as one comes out of a hypnotic trance, without leaving the slightest trace of it. How long did it last? He never found out the length of that indescribable state, although it would have been easy (or would it really have been?) to measure it simply by looking at his wristwatch. But he didn't want to know. . . It disgusts me to know. My senses would slow down on me, if I knew how long a flower lasted instead of looking at it.

"Theoretically it is possible," Hans repeated. "It is a fixed idea," Rafael said, irritated and fascinated at the same time. He raised his eyes from the big topaz that sparkled on Hans's left little finger. Hans was staring at him with the tiger-like eyes of one who spies without knowing it.

"Others before you have wanted the same thing," Rafael said. "To create a living organism with all its marvelous complexity, from its simplest cell to the one of greatest structural intricacy, has been the dream of a legion of people. But until now the only thing they have done is to fail miserably. . .

"Until now," interrupted Hans raising his voice, "they haven't accomplished it because they work with instruments that are too complicated as well as too crude. . .And because their knowledge is fragmentary. To find out the secret of the ritual dance to which chromatins submit before cell division by way of a superelectronic microscope is not enough; their theoretical bases and coarse dyes are not enough. For this and other things, dyes that have passed through a process of continuous ultrarefinement are needed."

"You are referring to the alchemical refinement method."

"What else would I be referring to? Of course! The difference between them and me, is that they work with substances and I work with **the** substance. Ultraelectronic microscopes! To think that the existence of that rather useless gadget smothers them with pride. Poor Doctor Nirenbuer! Believe me, the deeds of poor Doctor Pelc grieve me. No. No, my dear friend. To contemplate the intrinsic subtlety and, what is more important, the secret force of the DNA molecule, you need an instrument that functions with immensely subtle force. Do you understand me? Let's look for things with the proper equipment. Isn't it true that to examine a tiny mark on a silver teaspoon, you use a powerful magnifying glass and not the eyeglasses of a person with an astigmatism? But they look for life, and even for its cause with binoculars."

"All right. Or with toothpicks." Rafael agreed adding, what do you propose now? I ask because it seems you mean to tell me, whether or not I want to know.

"Don't you want to listen to me?"

"I prefer not to listen to you."

"You have to. . .and you are going to listen to me because you are less isolated than I. . .because you have ties with something. . . Because today, precisely today, I need to unite myself at all cost. . . Because I need to show my pride, as an act not of contrition but of humility.

Hans spoke with a hoarse voice, as he generally did when emotion overcame him. Rafael, shaken, sat up to listen to him.

"What do I propose now? . . .Now. . .hum. . .now. To say now is to not know anything about me. . .But it's not your fault. I have lived so many centuries. . .that I have forgotten so much. . .There is so much about me that I do not know! . . .Yes, you do not know, you will never know how much, because even for me all that is a profound mystery. . . But that doesn't interest anyone not even me. The important thing is that I wouldn't know what I know if. . .Time. . .yes, yes, a lot of time is needed. My dear friend, a lot of time. . ."

Rafael looked at Hans' pale but fresh complexion, his bright blue-black hair, his eyes those of a young forty year old, tigerish, and changeable like those of a illuminati. For the first time he surprised himself by taking seriously what Hans had said so often: "I have lived so many centuries!" He asked himself once again when that man had accumulated so much and such complicated knowledge. It all seemed miraculous. How could he know so much at forty? Was Hans forty, four hundred, or a thousand years old? Strangely enough he felt the need to ask a question, but contained himself. He was aware that Hans was following his inner movements with his penetrating eyes.

"You know another reason why you have the honor and obligation to listen to me? Don't ask me why. . .Because you are able to live in silence and with delight. . .That is why you are one of the few living people whom I almost love. . ..and I admire."

Hans smiled. Before that first smile (he was now aware that he had never seen Doctor Hans Arnin smile before, much less laugh), Rafael could not avoid being invaded by an undefinable something. This was because Hans was transfigured. That smile transformed him into a fallen angel, profoundly seductive and haunting, with something in common with the angels that didn't fall from grace. It was an overwhelming revelation because it revealed another one. This man must have loved once. . .

"Yes, listen to me well," Hans was saying. "For many, many years I have been looking for the secret to the butterfly. . .I want to build one from its very foundation to the tips of its wings. Are you stunned, dear partner, that I do not want to build a man, cell by cell? Does it seem strange that I focus my power and actions on a being apparently inferior to the 'king of creation'?"

"There are no inferior and superior creatures. There are only different ones. Their difference rests only in their degree of beauty."

"Exactly. Said more precisely: in the beauty of their essence."

"You want to be like God."

"Don't you?" answered Hans, as usual, with another question.

"At one time I sought enlightenment," mumbled Rafael.

"What is the difference?"

"You crave power. I wanted to integrate my infinitely small being into the infinitely grand Whole. I sought in alchemy what you are seeking. But you, following your way, will not get what you want. I, following my way, have reached it."

"You are not listening to me. That's why you challenge an artist who doesn't want to and cannot except a challenge."

"Let me be childish. . .Who isn't childish sometimes?"

"That's not childishness but alienation. Something must be the matter with you, something not strange but extraordinary, for you soliloquize to such a point that you do not see that I am using the verb in the past tense."

"Did you solve your koan?"

"No," Rafael said.

"Do you think you will?"

"I think I will never solve it. I neither am nor will ever by able to be a Zen painter. No matter what I do, I cannot manage to give up aesthetic pleasure. My mind and my spirit do not succeed in catching hold of the exaltation of the koan, being too attracted by the presence of beauty."

"Have you given it up?"

"Yes," said Rafael without any bitterness.

"Does it bother you?"

"No, I have my painting. I'll go somewhere with it. Some door or various doors, or maybe no door will finally open for me; but that is my road and the one I must follow. . .My error lay in going along one that didn't belong to me. But perhaps that was not an error, but only a necessary and foreseen movement."

"What do you mean?"

"For two years I noticed that the more I got into the pathway of the koan, the more it bound me to aesthetic pleasure rather than separating me from it. . .until I united with it in such a way that we have become one and the same thing. . .I. . .A spiritual state, while on the canvas I make the animation that never ceases to come alive. The mystery of the koan did not give me Nirvana, but it did give me the center of my equilibrium on Earth. . .And I foresee that something else which I perhaps will never know. . .The designs of the Divine are inscrutable."

"So now you are only a painter," Hans observed underlying the adverbs.

"Only a painter," Rafael said smiling with his strong and pure face in such a way that to Hans he seemed to be joking.

"You don't want any more?" insisted Hans not wanting to place importance on the jesting smile.

"No. I am satisfied with more modest pleasures. I think I have become extremely wise. I want to be the dragonfly's brother. Or its equal, at most. But not its actual and spiritual father. I am saved.

"Saved from what?"

"I do not run the risk of joining the legion of desperate ones who burned their wings. . .

Hans rushed forward. His immense long hand grasped the painter's wrist. They looked at each other. They were two powerful forces that repelled and attracted each other simultaneously. Han's hand kept pressing the wrist of the man who was his enemy more than ever.

"Listen," Hans said. "Don't you know that there are still a multitude of unknown molecules and that I know some of these unknown molecules. And that is not all. . . .For years scientific minds have asked themselves how genes duplicate themselves thousands of millions of times to inhabit thousands of millions of our cells. And I have the answer to that extraordinary question. . .Yes, yes, my dear friend. . .I have it. . .and many others. . . For example, the fundamental one about the make-up of the butterfly."

Rafael freed himself from the fist that was around his wrist like a tourniquet. Hans unbuttoned his tunic collar, while the sweat ran down his forehead.

"What follows I will tell you in a few words," Hans said standing facing the painter, with his arms crossed on his chest, and his eyes slightly closed as if he wanted to concentrate his strength on Rafael.

"What follows is this," he continued: "As you know the master DNA molecule is the one that knows how the nails, the heart, and, in short, all parts of a living organism are made; and it is another protein molecule, the RNA that transmits to the ribosomes the information that the DNA molecule gives it so that they produce the proteins living organisms are made of. You also know that until now, the molecular mechanisms of information of DNA or RNA and from the latter to the ribosomes has not been known. Well then, would you be surprised to find out that I discovered it? Do you realize that whoever knows this can do a great deal?. . . With that key in hand, everything is child's play. . .Yes, a simple child's game of reading the formula of the amino acids of a butterfly whose species died out five thousand years ago. . .A delightful creature! I found it buried not very deep in a glacier. . .I was looking for something else and I found it. I was alone. I found it. . .and not what I was looking for. Its transparent, white, long wings. . .It's a question. . .of. . .Don't think that I simply want to resurrect it. It's a question of making a copy of that animal that lived thousands of years ago. . .To make one that still survives wouldn't make any sense. . .At least not for me. That is not all I know, but that is enough for you. . .for now. I'll only add one last lesson. . . You know that what produces the firefly's light is a special enzyme. . .Also you know that for many centuries man has asked himself why and how certain animals fly. . .I have succeeded in discovering that this phenomenon, like the cold light of insects, is also due to a special enzyme. . .And that the difference between the wings of a bird and those of a butterfly, for example, is the variations in the geometric arrangement of ultrapure substances. . .If you arrange them in a certain way, the result is an animal with wings of one particular species. What is more. . .this is the key not only to the wings but to the whole of living creatures. Every one of their parts owes its function and form to a specific geometric arrangement of matter. The so-called "Geometric Formula" by which DNA, RNA, and ribosomes work and communicate to one another, is only a number and pure geometry. . .I left alchemy when I had reached the second from the last step because what interested me was not its ultimate end but its means. . .And because the movement of all living beings began to fascinate me. . .the atomic game, molecular agitation. . .the cell capable of realizing two thousand different actions per minute and in which, consequently, time is destroyed by the speed and the simultaneity of the movement that occurs within us and of which we are not aware. . .This is my obsession. . .Movement elevated to mathematical regions that can only be dreamed because the numbers that govern them are a supreme equation. Do you understand now why I went to biochemistry, to physiochemistry, to molecular biology and other things equally captivating?. . . The rest was natural and came by itself. The years of suffering do not bother me because now I know. . ."

Hans bent over suddenly and he said in a low hoarser voice, bringing his lips up to Rafael's ear as if someone else could hear him:

"I'm going to show you something. It doesn't matter if you talk about what you are going to see because no one will believe you. Come."

They went over to an immense iron door. In the huge vaulted room, covered with a metal Rafael could not identify, there was only, in the middle, an apparatus that seemed to be. . .What did it seem to be? Perhaps an enormous camera?

Rafael could not find out what the object resembled because Hans pressed a button and everything came into view. What absorbed Rafael's attention was not the glassy looking material in which two submerged disks of a nebulous consistency swung, as if rocked by a breeze, over structures resembling high tension towers. Something even more extraordinary made him stare at a certain point: a round, vertical, liquid looking mirror held up by two spheres; and a ray of light reflected inside the mirror. Hans pressed another button and the scene changed. . .Illuminated by the ray, a geometric form emerged that moved symmetrically from one point of the mirror to another while, intermittently, discharges of a whitish blue light sprang from it in quantum rhythm.

"The carbon atom," explained Hans. "Life springs forth from the electrons that form its valence. . .You are looking at the most powerful atom on earth. . .The form that gives birth to the vital spark. . .To see it is to contemplate the first day of creation. Behind that mirror there is a laboratory where various carbon atoms actually are working. . .

Rafael felt dizzy when he suddenly noticed that everything he was looking at had grown so big that it reached enormous proportions and had filled a space much greater than the room which he was in. . .And that all the forms seen were illuminated by their own light, with a dark and throbbing atmosphere.

Shaken, he turned to look at the flashing atom that was moving inside the mirror.

As they returned to the laboratory, Rafael, overcome by a sensation of nausea, felt that he was trembling inside.

They bid each other good-bye without speaking. He went out into the cool dusk air, as if he were penetrating for the first time the visible world where men moved. He felt estranged from everything that surrounded him. He almost did not recognize the almond tree that had always been at the right of Hans' house. . .He identified it moments later, but he didn't discover its meaning. It was hard for him to convince himself that the street lamp was not a hallucination, nor was the long tailed, long eared dog lying across the middle of the sidewalk, with its front legs stretched out parallel like a sphinx. The objects and beings had sunken into the reality of the beyond. He decided to walk home. Perhaps there he would find something to hold on to. . .Something that would return him to the beautiful and simple world to which he belonged, that world with a veil that hid the mystery. He had to find it before turning the key to the door of his house. He felt that if he fell asleep in this state of awareness of the profound irreality of reality, he would not wake up the same person. He turned in the opposite direction of his house. He stopped in front of an antique shop window. From the middle of the window a Byzantine figure framed in gold stared at him, a king of spades who in his left palm held a globe in whose center there was a triangle with an eye inside of it, and who in his right palm held a transparent globe that had a bright scepter inside. On top of the sphere a crown shone. The king of spades stretched out both hands while both globes whirled vertiginously. The king lowered one of his eyelids and then the other. His two eyelids reached the floor. Rafael looked inside the store. The antique dealer was watching him with kind but slightly cloudy eyes. Rafael walked away slowly and then started running.

Exhausted, he stopped beneath a tree on the big avenue, which was rather deserted at that hour. He leaned against the enormous trunk and cast a glance around; he feared he would be seen in that state but soon he was put at ease; the tree had a lot of shade and the closest passerby was a paper vendor who didn't seem particularly interested in selling his newspapers. "The Afternoon Telegraph," the paperboy kept saying in the mild voice of one who is talking to himself -- . . . "The Afternoon Telegraph with the latest news about the expedition to. . ."

Rafael saw the little boy holding a piece of string with which he was dragging. . .What was that wriggling on the ground at the end of the string? A little pile of string. The boy unexpectedly interrupted his almost inaudible hawking, and addressing the pile of string, mumbled: "You'll see, horse, you'll see when we get to the magic island with the tree that sings, the bird that talks like us, and fruits of beautiful pearls that. . ."

Rafael was fascinated by the little boy who was walking away with his "horse" -- the pile of string. He felt that he had been returned to the world, to the happiness of not participating in the unknown. Almost overwhelmed by the joy, he walked over to the park. There, several men were discussing the upcoming election. He was surprised to see that he was listening attentively to a political debate, which had never interested him before. For the first time that day, he felt he was a man like everyone else. He was almost overcome by his sudden happiness. He wanted to embrace and kiss those men in that town meeting.

"Buy goldfish," said the little voice. The little voice put down the hoop and lifted the bowl.

"Don't they shine?" asked the boy lifting the glass bowl so that the fish shone in the light of the park.

"They shine a great deal and they are very beautiful. Where do they come from?"

"From different rivers and from a place called India. . .that doesn't exist," replied the boy whose face lit up when he mentioned a place that didn't exist.

"It doesn't exist and that's why it's so wonderful. . .and it had shiny fish and unusual flowers."

"What size?"

"The size of your mother's parasol."

"My mother doesn't have a parasol. The only person that has one is the lady of the flower shop."

"Well then, the size of the parasol of the lady of the flower shop." Rafael took out a big new bill.

"Give me the goldfish."

Rafael watched the boy go away jumping and rolling his hoop.

He dreamed that he had dreams that Hans was taking him to a black and pulsating atmosphere. He woke up startled; he felt sick again, without knowing. . .but no. . .There on the drawing table, the fish were swimming in the bowl. He had not dreamed.

He felt something in his heart. . .As if it had grown in size and become heavy. He reached out his arm to get his robe. He felt the bones in his arm, from the humerus to the phalanges. How strange! How can you feel your bones that way! How? Rafael tried to analyze his sensation. Did his bones hurt? No. They didn't hurt. Did they feel good? No, not that either. They simply were there. . .It wasn't pain or the lack of pain that made him conscious of them. What was it then? He remembered that. . .I think it is Wednesday. . .I haven't eaten since Monday. . .I have hyperesthesia because of the fasting. . .That's all. . .How silly of me!. . .

In the park restaurant, which was rather deserted at this hour, there was an elderly couple at their customary table. She was very sweet, with her big mole painted on her cheek, and a brimmed hat to protect her from the sun, or whatever.

He felt cold. He asked for hot red wine. He noticed that he didn't feel his bones. When he tasted the earthy, innocent, joyous wine, which said nothing to his cells, it seemed the best wine in the world. Doctor Hans Arnim. . .I will never have another glass of wine. . .I will never want that benefit that lasts so briefly and is reserved for so few. . .You can drink it with all the devils that menace you, except me. He raised the glass and toasted with no one, or with the air, and said: "To your health!" He noticed that the little old lady was looking at him suspiciously on the sly. . .She must think that I'm crazy. . .So what? I also think she is crazy.

The waiter was waiting. The truth was Rafael wasn't hungry.

"Bring me anything and the newspaper."

A blue butterfly passed through the park. Rafael looked away. . . "Again Hans!" he said irritated; but an instant later he was looking for it in spite of himself and following it intently. Suddenly it seemed that the birds and flowers were visions of birds and flowers. . .That the trees were not trees but metaphors of trees that existed far away. The park. . .The park wasn't unreal in the customary way. Why did the jets of the nearby fountain sound differently and separately like syncopated notes?

He fixed his eyes on the newspaper. The word struck him like lightning. There in big letters it said, HANS. He unfolded the paper. He read:

"STRANGE DISAPPEARANCE."

The note was brief. It said:

"Today, at about three in the morning, the neighbors of Dr. Hans Arnim were awakened by the noise of an explosion. More than fifty people who left their houses to investigate were surprised by another explosion that seemed to come from the house of the mysterious doctor.

"While one of the curious went to call the police, the rest cautiously approached the house. They then heard the crackling of a fire and they noticed that the two rooms facing the street were brightly lit up."

Fixed into his chair, Rafael was sweating, unable to understand what he was reading. With great difficulty he continued,

"The firemen, armed with hoses didn't lose any time and broke down the front door. However, when they entered the completely deserted "burning" rooms, they found that there had been no fire, although the temperature in there was extremely high."

"Convinced that Dr. Arnim had been the victim of some accident, they searched for him throughout the house and in the garden in the back, without finding a trace of him."

"Except for some broken glass, no other damage was evident."

"It is possible that Dr. Arnim was not there at the time of the strange explosion and the even stranger "fire," but if that is the case, why hasn't he returned home yet? All the morning papers reported the event. At the time of this evening edition -- 5:30 p.m. -- Dr. Hans Arnim still has not appeared. On the other hand, if the accident surprised him at home -- a fact that is probable since, according to his neighbors, he never went out at night -- why was no trace of the scientist found?"

"The doctor lived completely alone. He was not known to have any relatives and no clues in this connection were found among his papers. The neighbors have stated that only occasionally did he receive callers."

"What is at the bottom of this mysterious disappearance? The police are actively working on the case."

The park had moved away. It was a park seen through binoculars. Or was it that his eyes had sunken to the back of his head. Who, besides himself, were Hans's friends? Who was Hans Arnim? Where was he? Rafael thought he knew.

The park had moved away. There, in the center of the lenses, he located all of its inhabitants. The animals and the plants hit his eyes simultaneously, as if they had come together in his pupils, or as if he were in the whole park all at the same time. He stayed still as the overwhelming consciousness of his bones invaded him. He looked for someting that might put him in the physical center of the park, which was now converted into the center of the universe. He vaguely saw a plate containing something. He found to his surprise that he could lift the fork. He put it aside with disgust. If he could lift the fork, then. . .He didn't dare to say "I can go." He simply said, "I must go."

He put one foot on the ground with all of his strength. He stood up completely. He began to walk along the lane, while the park moved away with him, as if both of them were being spied upon through a telescope by a third party. He saw his house moving away with every step he took. It was moving away like the park and himself. How long would it take him to get there? Nevertheless he moved forward, stepping firmly and looking carefully where he stepped. . .Where was his left foot? He noticed that he couldn't see his own outline very clearly. He realized that his bones were getting lighter. He jumped across the street.

Who was putting the key in the lock of the door? It was he! At last! He entered. His iliac bone had become so thin that he was as slender as a wafer. A little later he dissolved along with his skeleton which was scattered across the room. Now he felt as light as the day and caressed from within his flesh. He tried to look at himself on the outside. . .He couldn't see a thing. He looked at himself on the inside. He saw a luminous hole which was himself.

There was the paper in its stand and the elastic brush. He got up from the floor and leaned on the air with one finger. With a hand that felt nothing, he took the brush, wet it, and began to draw "a summary of the most beautiful memories of life." He concentrated on a flower and put down the bright yellow that gladdens all the animals. He thought about the winds that carry off the smell of all things and the form of everything they touch, and pilgrims' song beneath the sun. And the tree was created, infused with the spirit, resonant and lost among the animals that fly. And that tree was contained in a flaming flute that surprised the travelers.

And, all of a sudden the heavens appeared in body and soul to him. The brush flew before his illuminated hand; his hand flew pursued by a spirit that sprang from the air and from the fire and from the earth and from the water, and it covered the walls of the butterfly and its grand suspended nakedness. White, mobile, spread across the face of the world, the butterfly stood out and varied like the sun, flashing invisibly among the songs, like a palace of bubbles. A host of sparkling beings that reflected its wings followed it.

It was done. The brush dropped from his hand.

He was awakened by the sunlight coming in the closed window and the profound joy of the day following creation. Bewildered he looked at the sheet of paper. . .He sat up with a start. There was the tree and the yellow that seemed about ready to end soon, and also the daylight. The butterfly had disappeared. Troubled he looked away from the painting. Had he dreamed he painted a butterfly worthy of the sun? Was it an illusion of his overexcited spirit?

He fixed his eyes again on the painting and saw. . .Yes, there was no doubt. . .On the yellow, like a very brief vibration, there was a void identical to the body of the chosen one. That was its outline. In the place where its wings had been, a luminous spot still could be seen. He pressed his head with hands. . .I am sick. Wretched, wretched me, so inferior to your dreams. How could I think that that substance in movement, that the passing of nothingness to perpetual mobility of the air, could be true? God, make me some day just like one of my dreams.

Downcast, he went over to the table to look more closely at it. On it, in its stand, the tree, lost among the animals that fly, was looking at him. He went closer yet. It seemed that the surface of the table had an unusual shine. . .But he didn't investigate its source, being absorbed in the contemplation of his piece of art. . .I'll only look at the tree and the empty space. . .where I thought I gave it life. . .I'll never look at anything else. . .

The brilliance concentrated itself on one rainbow-hued transparent point. It was then that he saw it and bent over to look at it with the eyes of a possessed man. There was only a rainbow-hued, transparent chrysalis, broken a few seconds before but still humid.

He opened the window and lowered his eyes, for he knew that he could not look at it and still live.

In that very moment, the painter saw his body again. He, like the trace of the chosen one, had appeared in the world.

Eunice Odio, a homeless writer

by *Rima Vallbona*
Translated by Roberto Olivera

Eunice Odio lived for many years in Mexico, where she died in the most pathetic conditions and almost unknown in the literary circle of Costa Rica.

She is today known as a poetess.[1] Her outstanding talent has also shown itself, nonetheless, in works of prose filled with authentic artistic dedication, especially in essays on literature and art, and in short stories.

All throughout her essays we are drawn into the fascinating personality of the writer, we are told of her rebellious and passionately truthful nature, and shown to appreciate her intellectual preference, her vast culture and her intuitive understanding of the mechanism of the language. In terms of poetic achievements, Eunice Odio, along with Claudia Lars, finally opens the road for Central American women writers in the universal, innovatingly lyrical field.

Eunice Odio published only two small books in prose, **The Butterfly's Wings**, (5) a short story, and **In Defense of the Spanish Language**, (6) an essay. The rest of the work has appeared in various publications in Guatemala, Mexico, Venezuela and other countries.

She established a marked difference between prose and poetry. For her, "the task of the novelist and the writer of short stories must be centered around the analysis and not, as in the case of the poet, in the synthesis." (6, p. 24)

Her essays and other writings help us have an idea about the forms that this writer defended and fought for in the field of narrative prose. Her opinion is specially definite in regard to her characters: she rejects those that are "stereotyped repetitions of other authors' characters, and even of real life." (4, p. 121) She also considers that too much description and dialogue can kill the characters of a novel. There is no need to explain them. One must just allow them to act. (1, p. 70)

Eunice Odio wants the writer of a story to be original and deep, to show good humor, audacity and imagination. For her, audacity and orginality must be shown not only in the "novelty of the themes but in knowing how to treat them, even the ones from remote ages, so that they become contemporary again." (2, p. 121) Imagination, for her, has little to do with that "excess bound to deform;" it calls for a gift: to be able to give the stories endings that are "both surprising and ambiguous," which forces the reader [to become] the writer's accomplice." (2, p. 121)

------

[1]The first poems of Eunice Odio, in which her lyrical line is manifested — although still along traditional images —, appeared in **Repertorio Americano** between 1945 and 1947. During this time she won in Central American the "15 de Septiembre" award with her book of poems

[3]Terrestial Elements, which was published in Guatemala in 1948. In 1953 she published in Argentina **Twilight of Dawn**. And in 1957 her masterpiece appeared in San Salvador, **Journey in the Flames**

The **Butterfly's Wings** and "Once There Was a Man," the two stories included in this anthology, are related by means of the butterfly, "the chosen one," a key device and a mood controlling symbol in both stories.

The **Butterfly's Wings** is a little book published first in the Venezuelan literary magazine, **Zona Franca**.[2] Later on, it was published in Mexico as a book without date.[3]

In **Journey in the Flames**, one of her books of poetry, Eunice Odio tells of the horror the Creator, Ion, feels when he realizes that he is a being bound by his plurality since he contains all his fellow-men in himself, and is at the same time all of them. Quite the opposite is the case of the painter in **The Butterfly's Wings,** who has tried all the roads of Zen in order to reach Nirvana and ends up telling his friends, the scientist:

> I was so bound by aesthetic pleasure in itself that I finally merged
> with it in such a way that we are now one and the same thing. . .I. .
> one part of the soul, creating on canvas the animation that never
> ceases.

It is through art and not the mysticism of Zen, that the painter accomplishes the integration of his being "so infinitely small, into the All, infinitely vast". The transubstantiation of the painter in his own work is seen in the blindingly white butterfly, called the "chosen" because it was the supreme creation of his brush.

In the story called "Once There Was a Man,"[4] the narrator has gone beyond her neo-romantic mystic-pantheistic conception, and has innovated it with a Kafka-type attitude. Besides, this is also the moment when her fancy narrative approach becomes fused with the very heart of the Mexican reality, which is Latin American as well.

This second story is apparently the positive side of Kafka's "Metamorphosis" because it restates the theme of man's alienation, man's life oppressed by work and hunger, but with a process of liberation which ends up, supposedly, in the most beautiful metamorphosis.

As far as its narrative is concerned, this story starts to unfold in the so well known way of folktales with "Once upon a time. . ." However, the traditional code is crushed right away by an odd linguistic twist: ". . .Once upon a time **there was** a man who **will be**." It is a powerful way to bring in suspense. From that very beginning the reader is caught, his interest is aroused. The first sequence in the story starts with those words said by the "Flame man" and the possibility of the transformation is set up.

-----

[2]Eunice Odio, "The Butterfly's Wings," **Zona Franca,** 58 (June 1968,8-13).

[3]In the "Minimal Bibliography" of Eunice Odio which appeared in her anthology **In the Twilight of Dawn and other Poems**, this book was dated in 1970, a fact that cannot be found in the original edition.

[4]This short story was published in 1970, but it was written in December 1965, before **The Butterfly's Wings,** according to the author in a letter to Mr. Juan Liscano, Director of **Zona Franca**. (3, p. 155)

In the way the story is told the reader is also participating and can, at the end, finish the sentence he first read: Once upon a time there was a man who will be. . .a butterfly. Actually, the blue butterfly, in mind, is known scientifically as *Celastrina Argiolus* or *Spring Azure*.

Pedro's character traits force the reader into more suspense when one realizes he is at the moment living in an atmosphere of absurd everyday situations. Pedro tries, very hard throughout the story, to carry out his depressing task of ragpicker, but he is prevented from doing so by strange sensations: "His head felt so large! So utterly round! Besides, for the hundredth time, he had shed a large piece of skin." The following day, when he tried his pants on, he noticed that "they were extremely illfitting for him. As if they were somebody else's, as if he himself were someone else." Then he looked at his hands, now "covered with a light blue powder. . .celestial blue" which flowed down his arms.

Mingled in the action these mini-sequences are progressively stating a double process, simultaneous and contradictory: metamorphosis - redemption/hallucination-degradation. As in Kafka's work, this story displays a great break from the traditional literary form when it mingles the subjective vision of the world with the essence of objective reality into an allegory. But in Eunice Odio's story the allegory does not cover degradation but also redemption.

As far as the metamorphosis-redemption is concerned, we find stages in the life cycle of the butterfly clearly outlined. In the first stage of the transformation we see that Pedro "could not bring himself to accept the fact he had hairs growing in his eyes." One of Pedro's odd traits shows us the second stage, the beetle stage: Pedro felt the "strange sensation that his body was divided in parts [. . .and that his head] was very large, completely round and shiny." The third stage, the one concerning the cocoon, is obvious:

He wouldn't take off his clothes before getting in bed. He couldn't. Everything that covered his body was very close to his skin and it was caressingly warm. He lay there as if in limbo, falling upward, as if he had never been born or awake. The great sunny river made him appreciate his nakedness. All weaknesses had left him. And he attempted to move suddenly, violently. And his suit tore open on his shoulders, but he did not do anything about it.

Finally, when dawn came, he was out of the misery-cocoon:

"nothing was holding him [. . .] He ran around that morning filling his lungs with fresh air. He didn't wait for the bus. He didn't need it. He was faster than buses, more agile than kids [. . .] For the

first time he didn't know what to do [. . .] He walked for a while
[. . .] He noticed that he saw everything for the first time [. . .] He
rejoiced at the fact that he had a lot of space all to himself.

On the other hand, the tone-setting description in the story that deals with
poverty, overbearing work, filth, and lack of communication makes Pedro
embody the man who is suffering a progressive hallucinatory psychosis during
which he believes that all the changes necessary to become a butterfly are at
work in him.

As in Kafka's work, the method the narrator relies on is the parable.
According to Ernst Fisher, this method, by using make-believe exaggerations,
produces an artistic detachment, a distance that helps us make the world of
alienation even more obvious, as we give more emphasis to the absurd
monstruosity of everyday occurrences. (11, pp. 119-24)

When dealing with the relationship among characters in the story's
structure, the critic Bremond considers the narrative sequence in terms of "a
degradation" - a deficiency that grows worse — or an "improvement" — a
degradation that grows better. (9. p. 92) In this sense, when we look at Pedro's
character traits, "Once There Was a Man" denotes an evolutionary process in
its redeeming metamorphosis, but the atmospheric signs mark the presence of a
degradating hallucinatory psychosis. This means that there has been a break in
one given series of events. Ordinarily, improvement and degradation cannot
take place by the same agent. As the narrative continues there appears a double
direction, simultaneous and opposed in itself: the more painful and difficult the
struggle of the ragpicker in his monotonous daily work, the better his situation
gets in the progressive sequences that go side by side with the development of
the butterfly, which attains total metamorphosis — a retribution to his
sacrifices and suffering, a form of redemption.

This double action creates a tension made up of homologous relationships.
So, following the parable's method, the dreamlike quality of the story acquires
a neorealistic dimension in which the theme of metamorphosis is at the same
time the theme of alienation, while the butterfly, as a symbol of rebirth, turns
into a cognitive purifying element through fire-hell-work.

As far as the language is concerned , these two sources become intimately
mingled in the likely unit of unlikely verbs which from the beginning express
strange states of mind, and which can also correspond to a hallucinated
condition: "he was horrified", "he noticed", "he felt bad yesterday", "he felt
something again", "when noticing his helplessness", "every one of his bones
was shaking", "that odd sensation grew", "he was overwhelmed by a feeling
of nostalgia and oppression", "he stopped thinking", "he was only aware of an
enormous relief."

It is in this way that the story starts. And it does not stop there. It grows and
gathers strength in the retrospective sequence about Pedro's childhood, when

Father Gabriel sends Pedro home and the latter says, "Didn't you yourself tell me that the Master called Pedro? And you, my own, are throwing me out?" From this very moment, Master-Christ/Disciple-Pedro are the subjacent key components in the whole story which give more sense to the metamorphosis-redemption.

We must also add that the time in which the event takes place — Monday and Tuesday, with a few flashbacks into Saturday and Sunday — brings the details close to everyday reality, and it confirms the fact that something definitely irregular has happened to Pedro. His own two sisters vouch that he did not get home the night before, but his friends at work say they have not seen him since Saturday. While the others start looking for him, Pedro himself decides to dig out his own answers, and in that search he begins to climb a tree. Once on top of the tree, resting on the laurel's leaves, the butterfly-Pedro opened his wings "and laid down. It had the color of God and laid very still. The sleeping butterfly."

"Once There Was a Man" is in the category of outstanding works of the avant-garde movement, since in this story we find a decisive, immediate attitude towards the reality of our own time and our underdeveloped countries, but no criticism of it. With this story, Eunice Odio finds her place among those writers who, paralyzed by anguish - according to Lukacs (12, p. 99) — decide to handle the immediate phenomena of the deceiving and covered-up socio-historical reality without criticizing it. Within the line of Latin American literature, this moment in her narrative falls into the category of what the writer Antonio Cándido called "the moment of a receding catastrophic conscience", which shows a definite change among the writers on the continent since 1930. (10, p. 337) It should be noted that **The Butterfly's Wings** on the contrary, stands for the preceding stage, that of "pleasant backward attitude, which goes hand in hand with the idea of 'new place' and of privileged surrounding" attitude that has been in our literature since the time of the colonies (10, pp. 335-337). The story belongs among those of science-fiction; it follows, in its inspiration, types of literature that are alien to us. It is a piece of work disconnected from our immediate reality and full of neo-romanticism. The excess of informative dialogue gives to these pages a dramatic and didactic tendency which eliminates the narrative essence, the gradation, the tension and the ambiguity that are basic characteristics of current short stories. Also, **The Butterfly's Wings** is a story without social or historical perspective. Thus, it lacks the dynamism of "Once There Was a Man."

Due to the high quality of her lyric poetry, Eunice Odio has earned a special place in Latin American literature, although she has not been accorded the status she deserves.

As far as her prose is concerned, it should be evaluated in its totality in order to better understand her literary zeal and the accomplishments of her talent in the various genres she undertook. The rather incomplete analysis I have given reveals her up-to-date position among writers who know how to handle the elements that are needed to tell a story of our time in an open way, just by stating our immediate reality and without criticizing it. She leaves in this way many of her countrymen behind, all those who although better known than she, were rather limited in their experiments.

All her works, her poetry as well as her prose, have the stamp of universal authenticity. She deals in a cognitive language, "which derives its strength from semantics and metaphysics, slightly related to the original." (8, p. 66)

There are many reasons behind Eunice Odio's work to move us to undertake a detailed and objective evaluation of her production: her authentic and universal approach, her literary vocation based on solid integrity, and the mastery with which she handles expressive elements and techniques. She should no longer be excluded whenever we talk of Latin American literature.

BIBLIOGRAPHY

WORKS BY THE AUTHOR.

1. Odio, Eunice. "Actualidad", **Revista Mexicana de Literatura,** Vol. 2, 12 (July-August 1957), 70-75.
2. —————. "Alberto Bonifacio Nuño: **Juego de espejos." Cuadernos** (March-April 1961), 121.
3. —————. **Antología - Rescate de un gran poeta** (Selection of texts by Juan Liscano) Caracas: Monte Avila Editores, C.A., 1975.
4. —————. "Carlos Fuentes: **Las buenas conciencias." Cuadernos** (September-October 1960), 121, 22.
5. —————. "El rastro de la mariposa". **Zona Franca** 58 (June 1968), 8-13. **El rastro de la mariposa.** Mexico: Alejandro Finistere Editor, n.d.
6. —————. **En defensa del castellano.** Mexico: Gráficas de Menhir, S.A., 1972.
7. —————. "Había una vez un hombre". **El Cuento,** 40 (January, February 1970), 216-28.
8. —————. "Nostalgia del paraíso". **Cultura,** 19 (January-February-March, 1961), 62-67.

TEXTS BY OTHERS.

9. Bremond, Claude. "La lógica de los posibles narrativos", in **Análisis estructural del relato.** Argentina: Editorial Tiempo Contemporaneo, 1972. pp. 87-109.
10. Cándido, Antonio. "Literatura y subdesarrollo", in **América Latin en su literatura.** Mexico: Siglo Veintiuno, Editores, S.A., 1972.
11. Fisher, Ernst. "El problema de lo real en el arte moderno", in **Polémica sobre realismo.** Buenos Aires: Editorial Tiempo Contemporaneo, 1972.
12 Lukacs, Georg. **Significación actual del realismo crítico.** Mexico: Ediciones Era, S.A., 1963.

3

YOLANDA OREAMUNO

YOLANDA OREAMUNO
1916-1956

Born in San José, Costa Rica, she was a year old when her father died.

Lacking a university career, she became a secretary and in 1936 married Jorge Molina Wood, a Chilean diplomat. They moved to Chile where she dedicated her time to writing. Soon after, her husband became ill and took his own life.

In 1937, Yolanda married Oscar Barahona, a Costa Rica lawyer. Their son, Sergio, was born in 1942 and three years later divorce came with a court fight for the custody of the child who was given to the father. This began her real Purgatory and exodus. In poor health and impoverished, she lived in El Salvador, Guatemala and Mexico. She was staying with her friend, Eunice Odio, when, very ill and poor, she died in 1956.

Among her many writings, scattered and lost, she wrote three novels, many short stories and articles.

In 1950 Guatemala published her prize winning novel, **La ruta de su evasión**.

After her death, Costa Rica decided to remedy its neglect of this outstanding writer, and gathered articles and short stories to publish under the title of **A lo largo del corto camino** (1961, Editorial Costa Rica, San José, C.R.)

In 1968, Victoria Urbano wrote the first book on Yolanda Oreamuno studying and analyzing her artistic accomplishments in the literary field. Ever since, many articles have appeared in the Costa Rican newspapers praising Yolanda's skills. Rima Vallbona has also written a condensed presentation of Yolanda Oreamuno and her works, which was published by the Costa Rican Ministry of Culture in 1972.

HIGH VALLEY

Translated by Martha ONan

A strange, unnerving heat wave had settled over the city and countryside.

Nothing more could be said except that it had stopped there and to move it away all that was needed was the help of any kind of wind but no wind came.

Things even had changed color. In cool weather, yellow does not annoy, nor red hurt, nor green comfort. They simply exist. But now the dry, dusty yellow full of hot ochre corners seemed to intensify the torrid sun's already excessive rays. The tremendous vibration which danced in the air found, in the red, surfaces favorable for multiplying and sending back more cruel and annoying reflections. People looked for green as a refuge and realized with surprise that there was very little green in the city.

The sun, perhaps from a phenomenon of the season or perhaps as a product of the torment which it inflicted, beat down all day from the zenith, all day in the middle of the street, all day looking for the vertical surface of objects in order to fall parallel to them, without pity, until it sank quite late, when all hope had been lost, between a red halo and a cloud of smoke which even took from it its unchangeable circular form.

Air — but why speak of air? — did not exist. To the molecules, myriads of particles of dust, fuzz, unidentifiable foreign matter and strong odors made the atmosphere unbreatheable almost solid, full of a humid, hot, tormenting quality.

The clouds of that always clear sky had fallen sagging in clumps over the city, and the moment when they would be scattered in rain and storm was both feared and desired. The feeling of the storm's nearness was so oppressive that the big-bellied, pressing clouds with bright, luminous centers and violent gray profiles were terrifying and the continuation of the agonizing period of heat was almost preferable to the cloud burst.

It could be that the clouds contaminated by the torrid climate would pour down scalding rain or they might be driven away by a burning wind, all of which in its horrible uncertain anticipation seemed worse than the oppressive existence of the heat. At present, they covered the sun without cutting off the punishing heat, and everything took on a dramatic gray color. The color the anticipation of the storm, the heaviness of the atmosphere weighed down on all persons, driving from their minds the sense of responsibility and bringing to their bodies an intense stirring that resembled suffering. It was horrible; it was morbid and was sublime.

20th of November Avenue with its tall skyscrapers, without a single propitious shadow or merciful color, repeated itself in several blocks as if it were endless.

"I'm sorry, **blondie**, but the next bus will not leave until six."

"With the four hours it takes to get there, that means arriving at ten tonight. That's impossible," said the woman.

She stood thinking.

"Is that the only way of getting there?"

"The only other way, **blondie**, is to hire a taxi. I can get one, but it will be expensive."

The woman hesitated. At that moment, a man she had not seen interrupted and she really didn't look at him then.

"I have as great an emergency as you. If you don't object, we both can share the taxi."

She thought only about her urgency.

"That's fine."

The man whose face she had not seen sat in front with the driver. Both talked about those dry subjects men discuss when there is a woman with them. He asked him about the land, the maguey, the Indians, eager to hear the answer in spite of the driver's crass ignorance; but the man seemed interested not in the driver's very inexact information but in the picturesque form of his expression, in his delightful Mexican accent, in the mixture of superstition and legend he used to explain everything.

The land for her was quite different from what the driver was saying. At least it was today. That drab land in the high valley kept the trace of having been lapped in past ages by something soft and trembling like the sea. Heaped-up little hills seemed to have been made lazily by indolent fingers which, right after having made them perhaps by caressing them, took away all sharp edges until they were smooth, small and round, and compact, and also without vegetation. Perhaps because the salty taste of water was still in them and the plants' sweet sap found no nourishment. One looked like the other. That strange softness of contour could only have come about through millenniums under water which slowly had dried up leaving the hills young and tender in a world of torment in which the very high mountain chains, older in age, wrinkled in time, bared down to the rocks by the high altitude, looked at them disdainfully from the august whiteness of their peaks. Those little hills of high valley shone strangely bare and infantile in comparison with the austere snow-capped peaks of Popocatepetl and Iztaccihuatl.

And today, under the furious sun, the hills still appeared more as flesh of the earth, armpits, curves of the hip, round thighs, chubby bodies, geographical hulks.

The woman thought that the heat increased if one looked at them mottled here and there by clay huts and by bristling maguey woods in geometric shapes.

Everybody in the taxi was suffocating. The scant air only helped raise the dust from the road and roll it inside in puffs.

The man had taken off his coat and turned back his shirt collar. Oppressed by the monotonous landscape, she slowly, with the meticulous slowness everything happened these days, plotted a parabola as she looked from the white horizon of mountain peaks, the sides of the hills covered with maguey, the endless curves on the road, the top of the car, and finally, to the man's neck. And her eyes stopped. Through them she made, first an observation, then a reference, then felt a response to what her eyes had not noted.

Her observation said: "That's a strong neck." And that was all.

Her inference said: "Under that thick, dark, slightly red skin move strong tendons, and tremendous muscles play. The impression of strength certainly does not come from the size of the neck, somewhat short, but from its straightness, firmness, its elastic obedience to the movements of the head and shoulders, its fullness narrowed at the base of the ears, the rich blood which could be seen flowing under the skin."

And her emotion said: "On touch that neck must have a consoling hardness. It must be stupendous to feel under one's fingers the smooth tension of the play of those muscles. The skin is probably rough, young, warm."

And then when imagination was already on the verge of adventure, reason arrived:

"But must I also let myself be dominated by the intoxication of this climate? Do I like everyone else now look boldly and inquisitively at things? Ordinary people go around showing an indecent desire for nudity, have tense bodies, sleeping souls, open feelings. But am I like that? Why must I think about a neck whose face I have not even seen? Why is an inquisitive voice important to me, an insistent voice which asks but with no interest in any answer but the ring of the word and the emotional springs that trigger it?"

When the man had turned away her stare on purpose and painfully, he moved; also with the slowness everything happened these days, as if it took quite an effort to move, he raised his arm and put it on the back of the seat. Her glance which continued fell heavy and submissive on his arm.

It was bare above the elbow. It was sinewy, broad; much whiter than the neck, and from the elbow on down, turbulent hair covered all parts, the blood more vital here, it seemed not to run in a web of small veins as on his neck but poured in fervent, blue river beds down to his hand, where it rushed raising the skin, making it palpitate, and where, with an intense, intimate, deep palpitation, vibrated all the tension of the man who let his hand fall in a quiet way, in an inert way, but inhabited by a ferocious vitality. As far down as his hand, the uncontrolled invasion of thick hair extended freely, without any order, on his skin.

The emotion of the day which she had difficulty in resisting voluntarily urged her to break away from reasoning.

"A hand for caressing or striking? For an affectionate touch or for taking the offensive? A hand for seizing an ax or for opening a book?" She didn't know. His hand resting there didn't reveal any refined tendency in itself. Only a wild vitality animated it. His arm didn't have the type of muscle developed in exercise, which is short, obvious, but a natural muscle which exists in its own right and shows up only when it is going to be used for something. And if some disturbance required use of the arm, the hair served to make it round when it was at rest and to disguise it when in action. Only by moving her attention past the dark curtain of hair did her glance come to realize the tremendous striking power and enormous elasticity of embrace which his arm had because of those muscles.

After having seen his neck and sensed his arm, she, prisoner of the horrible laxity of the day, wanted actually to experience them. With a strange urge to look at the man's face, hear his voice addressed straight to her, she felt capable of speaking to him in order to accomplish these two things. But still a fleeting conscience held her back. Largely by means of reasoned effort she stopped looking at the arm, stopped being concerned with the man, and tried to concentrate on other things.

The bare hills were passing by. From time to time, a town, which was not really a town but only a group of mud hovels, whizzed by totally beaten by the sun.

The Indians were men of earth, made of the same material as their mud huts, without any color or windows, because their eyes had no reaction to light and their entire expression was covered by the hermetic gloom of their way of living. The huts were of hardened mud, the Indians were also of hardened mud, a little darker, a little more mobile but equally static. The hot, red sun finally set, and the sultry clouds there on the final descent from the high valley, were, if that is possible, nearer the earth. Now along with the heat's endless punishment came the torment of the dust and from the fields mysterious noises so persistent that they were audible over the motor's roar.

She had not yet spoken. When was she going to? She was alone on an unknown road with two unknown men, and for the first time she realized that she had rushed into a foolish decision without thinking. How was it possible that in this foreign country, Mexico, without fear of any kind, she had risked a four-hour trip along an isolated road with two men, one of whom was an Indian corrupted by the city and the other a foreigner like herself, to judge by his accent and his voracious desire to ask questions? How was it possible? Only the unheard-of irresponsibility of recent days, the relaxing of her will power and reason which was caused by the heat could have brought her there, a hundred kilometers from the city, in a taxi which was eating up a road which could go somewhere. She who had done this could not understand why. Suddenly, overcome by the volubleness which everything had, her fears disappeared and she felt reconciled, almost happy for letting herself be taken along, while just one unimportant thought bothered her: "How will these scorched lands be watered, where do these silent Indians drink water, when is it going to rain and where will the water from the storm drain off?" The heat by the end of the afternoon had not diminished, and actually suffering became anguish and increased in intensity and frequence and struck everything, the thin cattle, the air, the few bare trees, and those people in the taxi. The wounded sun bled in the west.

She then became aware of her body. Everything was beating in her. She didn't know why. She felt the rush of her own blood, the feverish throb of her temples, the tingling of her nose; she felt she was holding her mouth open, and even though she wanted to, she couldn't stop yawning; she felt she was perspiring through everything and lifted her clothes lightly trying to dry them. Her hot legs bothered her where they touched. She put her hands on the seat. She put her head back and unconsciously heard the shortness of her breath and thought that the blistering air coming into her lungs was suffocating her. However, this slow suffocation didn't make her suffer, she felt a transmutation,being herself, of losing consciousness little by little and giving up to the heat without any effort, of becoming irresponsible and crazy.

The man had stopped talking. She, almost passed out, couldn't see him. Everything this past hour had ceased existing or being important.

A miss in the motor made her straighten up. The man also was alert and was looking out the front. The driver turned off the motor, put his taxi on the right side of the highway, and with an Indian's cold calm got out without saying anything. The man got out too.

She was now more afraid. Would they stay parked there with night upon them, many kilometers from the nearest town, without any means of leaving? But this fear in the midst of all her emotions that day was overcome by an interest which made everything lose importance. The man was standing by the car window in front of her, and she was finally able to look at him.

To describe him she would not have thought of the words which she had used to describe his neck or his arm. But through those strong virile features ran the same rich blood as in his neck, and in his temples, on his brow, the same fervent blue veins bore the man's obvious tension. For some seconds there was in his chestnut eyes a proud, dominating expression and also the fleeting appearance of great fatigue. Only for such an active, tractable, strong neck was the decided cut of his features suitable, the volubility of his smile made for dwelling on nothing, and the firm closure of his mouth made for keeping a deep, mature sadness. Only a hand like his could go with a forehead molded from pure bone, with stiff eyebrows, with an incisive chin, with a strong jaw. He was very tall, big chested, broad shouldered, and every part of him seemed a little tired.

Truthfully they had not really talked to each other before, because in spite of the fact that she had heard all during the trip his conservation with the driver, his voice sounded new, as if for the first time, when he approached the car window and said to her:

"Miss, I am sorry that it can not be repaired. The Indian refuses to abandon his taxi because he insists that tomorrow early a taxi-driver friend of his will bring him what he needs to repair it. You have two choices: risk going to the next town or spend the night here with the Indian. You must decide."

"But isn't there any way to make him go?"

"It's useless to try to convince an Indian who probably is used to being robbed and is afraid they will rob him. Just tell me whether to beat him or kill him."

His offer in a warm voice now without any inflection seemed to be a simple statement of what she would decide. He spoke so quietly, so reluctant to discuss, seek advice or suggestions that she was certain that the Indian could expect only a beating or death. She looked at the man's arm - capable of killing - his calm expression, just waiting for her decision so that he might carry out his offer, and , even before he asked, she looked him in the eye and said:

"I'll go with you."

And together they set out into the night which was beginning to fall.

How natural it seemed to her, under the burning cover of heat, to go along a strange road with a man whose name she didn't know!

And when he spoke, it was not for putting aside but for meeting squarely, as a logical fact, the odd situation.

"When I saw you at 20th of November Station I thought you were taller, and I thought also that it would be pleasant to have you as I do now beside me."

There was no impudence in his voice, there was no idea of touching her, there were no plots in his mind. He took things where they were, and from there went on as if they were always like that, and as if she, as he had, only expected what was happening.

And she, who always had judged herself severely, did not reproach herself when she answered with the spontaneity he invited:

"All during the trip I wanted to see your face."

The man heard her answer without being disturbed, turning smiling to her, as if smiling at a woman already loved and held in his arms, and without dwelling on the subject pointed out with his chestnut eyes the fields, highway, and clouds while saying:

"I always seem to have been waiting for an unexpected situation which for a moment at least would put me face to face with this openly hostile nature. The peaks of the volcanoes do not want to get along with this strange valleys; it is obvious that they have been at odds for centuries, and it is obvious even that the hills want to grow to become peaks and the mountains laugh at such a ridiculous effort. However, the enormous stretch of the valley makes it magnificent and diminishes the height of the mountains. If there were not so many of these small hills, if we had not passed kilometer after kilometer of them these past few hours, they would make us afraid, but with so much sun, they end up terrified. They feel like battling with ungrateful nature, breaking her like a loved woman, making her yield when she is exhausted, while she gets a bed and bread."

She would have liked then to be that woman for whom he would conquer the height of the summit and for whom he would tame the valley's sterility. And for him, even she wanted to be fertile.

They began to hear noises of the night getting nearer, sharp cries of strange birds which were unfamiliar to both of them, croaking of toads in remote flatlands, the sharp chirping of crickets calling for rain; there could be heard footsteps on the hard road, the furious evaporation of plants, the woody swaying of the trees, the vital movements of everything bound to the land by a strange imprisonment which at night, when the sun's rays do not expose them, writhe trying to break their bonds; there could be heard the distant silence of the valley, the poundings of their bodies side by side united in front of nature's hostility.

Already for quite some time she had given up to the heat's strange witchery. Already she had renounced defending herself. Already she had accepted as inevitable the fact that the body lives more intensely when nature struggles not to die, and she also knew that when nature suffers as in the present situation face to face with a climatic situation which always destroys it, the body becoming a victim like herself, defends itself and lives in the struggle much more than it lived before when everything was easy and there was no need to struggle. For that reason when he took her by the arm to help her along in the increasing darkness, she did not resist the powerful current which stirred her feelings, which numbed her hands and made her half close her eyes, but which made its presence felt jubilantly in her just as a glorious event which is going to happen. His gesture was not courtesy, nor was it indecent, it was the beginning of a communion.

"When summer comes in March in my country," she said living in faraway memories, "just as here, when the pastures are dry and the land cracked open from the heat the way they are here, cicadas sing in the mountains, trees twist, and every person and thing makes an all-out effort until rain bursts forth. Then, if it rains in the countryside -- because in the city rain is humiliating -- if it rains on the pastures and roads, the water is glorious, all plant odors come forth and create the desire of being naked and virginal."

And he, as if speaking for himself and of an anguish from long ago, said:

"With a drought delicate odors sleep. But strong plants give off an aroma, so do large flowers which open at night, and resin in tree trunks, and dust along paths. Human bodies smell bad with odors which in the daytime under normal conditions would bother us, and which under other conditions we enjoy like animals. I don't know whether on nights like these, plants smell like animals or we smell like plants."

He turned to her:

"I smell your aroma."

And nearer:

"Your skin is soft, the way I would want it. You have bright eyes and a large mouth. You have strong hands and long legs and full hips, the way I would like them. When you smile, you are completely genuine. When you look at something there are small yellow, diabolical specks in your eyes; when you touch, it is as smooth as the morning, as the earliest of mornings. You are everything I would want. You will be as fertile as the earth which comes alive again after the first rain. You will be as good as a child's smile; and brave as a mountain river; and as hostile as someone else's house to a strange man. You are everything I would want."

His eyes were fixed on hers in a vague dream. But he did not touch her.

The heat now was more oppressive than ever and was moving, rather swimming, in an almost solid element because of the humidity and drought. It was so intense and sullen that now clothes, sweat, dust were not at all important. Everything was inert: only two things were awake, imagination and the body.

Imagination was needed for seeing stars in the noisy night, through the clouds, and to find there a faint fluorescence which in reality surely did not exist. Imagination was needed for thinking about the strange embrace which in the heat plants would give each other. Climbing vines would look for tree trunks to make plaits and grow, crazy to reach the tree tops. Moss would creep over roots covering them with the soft, inexorable power of an ocean wave and would grow into their deepest folds and would get the sweet dampness which only roots in their dense structure were able to store in the heat; and roots would not be so bare and dry. The orchid's succulent and immodest petals would offer themselves open to the copula of pollen and insect; and would be white with edges inflamed in violet crimson. And all plants would in the compassionate night, which hides the shame of the drought, a crazy desire to grow, bloom, nurture seeds, scatter them in the wind, and die because of them. Because all inanimate things in the hot night become living beings, they forget that they are dying of thirst and unexpectedly are imprisoned in a wild frenzy of living and procreating. Female animals would fell to dark corners, certain of the male's victorious pursuit, and everything from the parched land to the last delicate leaf which was storing up the last drop of sap (small, just born) had a deep desire to be, exist, and reproduce. A pure desire, a simple desire, a natural desire, spontaneous; a normal course in the normal expression of normal acts.

Human beings on a night like this stopped existing as separate entities and became part of the whole of nature. There was not in the oppressive night lust or concupiscence, there was the realization of acts which civilization, mind, and the struggle for life have deformed to such an extent as to make them appear abnormal. And everything, just as a river goes to the sea, fell again under the natural law of nature on a night like this. The tree fell, the root, the flower, the land, the animal, and man.

And the two of them also, walking silently, were the flower and seed.

They had been walking a long, long time together. For some time he had assured her that it would always be this way. And for a long time, perhaps from the time she first saw him, she resignedly, with a jubilant resignation, had accepted everything that was to come.

"I have always loved trees," he said, "loved the rain, and I have hated myself when in the city, through artificial reasoning, the sun, rain, and wind bothered me. However everything was so absurd there that these simple things were in the way, just as human ugliness also was an obstruction. Here, in nature there are also ugly things, but nothing is in excess. the toad is ugly, and the land when it is dry and bare, and the grass eaten too low by horses, and trees in the midst of dropping their leaves; and birds are ugly when they are moulting, and the white maggot of the earth is ugly, and the black worm of the branches; ugly also are black beetles, screech owls, and spiders. In spite of so much ugliness, nothing shocks; in the harmonious concert that all make, I am sure that the humming bird does not find the scorpion ugly, nor the flower the root. Things are not ugly, the concepts we use to designate them are ugly."

He looked at the horizon and then said:

"It's going to rain, baby. You'll be soaked and I shall do nothing to prevent it because I want to see the water run from your hair, down your cheeks and into the deep corners of your mouth."

Everything was approved by her who earlier had defended herself by cold reasoning, and now she waited for him without impatience, with certainty and confidence.

"I want to see also how the water shrinks your clothes. No, I'll do nothing to stop that. It's good to see you like that, to find you like that, and to keep you always. You hear that, don't you? Today, you and I are no longer you and I, and the norm for our conduct will not be found in what people call morals. We are about to find it here, on the ground that we cross, in the mortal air which surrounds us, and in the dark countryside which encircles us. We can forget about responsibility for ourselves; today we belong to all this, and we must especially join nature in its great protest against the drought. If we men unite to fight against men; if we join together to struggle for ideas, then tonight when we are not men or ourselves, we must commune in the savage protest which nature initiates. If it rains now, you and I, baby, shall do what the trees do, animals or the grass, because tonight we are part of them. If the tree trembles from the water which bathes it, you will tremble because of me; if the grass grows when its thirst is calmed, you will do likewise next to me; if animals look for each other in terror of the storm, you will find yourself with me; and if they love each other, we shall love each other also."

Now already thunder began to rumble in the distance. Big-bellied clouds became bright in order to burst loose and there was in everything the great expectation which precedes the solution. It seemed that the plants turned away from the direction the wind was inclined to blow, and it seemed that the animals stopped harassing one another in order to become part of the general waiting. The earth opened, making wider and deeper cracks in order to welcome the torrential rain. Leaves lifted themselves up, became concave in order to hold the rain drops. Animals looked with luminous eyes at the night and dilated their nostrils as they smelled the storm.

The two on the edge of the road waited also. The man, who already could have had her had he wanted to, had not touched her. Because with the earth, with the storm and trees, he obeyed solely the great harmonies of the natural concert, and would bend over her when the branch under the weight of the water would bend not before nor afterwards.

Thus his words:

"You will get wet, baby; look how the rain is already beating down on the hills. The pasture lands will drink up the moisture, and I shall drink it in your face. This is the final struggle. It comes winning, victorious, to calm the great longing. If this were to continue forever, you and I also would wait forever."

Gentle splashes of rain had already reached the road which began to give off a maddening smell, and those delicate, faint odors which needed great purity of air to come forth at all gained dominance over the strong odors which had withstood the dust and drought. There was a smell of wet grass, tiny flowers, tender stalks, stems, water, and stars. A lemon aroma which certainly for days had been stored in the fruit and incapable of piercing its thick skin was quite evident. A violet perfume which certainly had been hidden in the roots came from below, wafting through the atmosphere. The smell of the white moss which certainly, during the drought was a source of moisture for the plant spread through the air. A fresh, healthy, young perfume went from the woman to him.

And when the first sheets of furious rain beat the land nearby, when lightening flashed there, and the streaks came closer, the man's benediction fell on her, and over the earth the water's benediction.

It had rained so much, so much the past night. It had rained so much that she, lying she did not know why in that narrow, small bed in the inn, did not know how she had arrived there.

But whom could she ask?

Melancholic thoughts which always tormented her bothered her conscience today as never before. They prevented her, and would always prevent her, from asking how she had arrived, and she would have to bear indefinitely that awful void in her memory with which she awoke.

After she had seen through the window that the hills were cleansed, that the flowers had opened unusually wide in the little hotel's garden, that a poor imitation of grass seemed to be wanting to break through the ground--revealing in its insipidity the shallow bed of its geographical location -- she left the room in order to try to find out with a minimum of questions where she was and the route she had to follow.

63

The garden dressed in Sunday clothes brought to her mind an absurd phrase: ". . .gentle as a morning."

This made her smile: where had she read that phrase? It sounded fresh and pretty, and also recent, but she did not have time to undertake such an absurd investigation just for a phrase.

She returned to her preoccupations.

THE TIDE RETURNS AT NIGHT

Translated by Catherine G. Bellver

The water around the boat has an oily consistency. Farther on where the sun's reflection blends sea and sky, it has a metallic quality. The strange absence of a horizon creates a humid and dark atmosphere like that inside of a bell.

In this stifling air, candles surely must snuff themselves out alone and sea gulls must die hurled against the perpendicular angle formed by the horizontal path of their flight and the vertical line of the sun.

Uninvited, dense smells penetrate the nose: from the nearby, but invisible earth, the perfume of sandalwood and from the damp and creaking deck, a smell of leather. The cables smell of tar, the footsteps of silence, the words of shouts, the women of salt, and the men of roots.

The boat does not move, and if it does, it moves with the slowness of the painful penetration into a solid mass; the people do not move, and if they do, they walk with the burden of a weight greater than gravity. Lianas tie feet to the floor and everything vertical -- arms, legs, hair and words -- inevitably falls. Islands of golden sand seem to emerge from the water where the keel will hopelessly come alongside. It is daytime, but it is night because things have the feline quality that darkness gives them and people feel the suspense, the lack of dimension, the irresponsibility, and the rawness that night produces. In spite of the humidity there is thirst. The passengers crowd the bar while they shrink from one another to avoid skin, breath, and sweat.

I am standing alone at the entrance. My cigarette smoke lingers in the air stratifying into solid blue scrolls. Holding a frosted glass in her hand, she looks at me from a distance. Then, suddenly, pushing away the air, cutting the horizontal line of our glances and breathing, and dividing in two the solidity of the air, like a boat, she approaches me. When we are side by side, she barely comes up to my shoulder and she must raise her head to speak to me.

"Come and have a drink with me."

The abruptness of the invitation from a stranger, the informality, the straightforwardness did not surprise me, because nothing is surprising in a motionless environment where instincts alone survive and where, to break the inertia, all movement must have the vigor of an assault. I keep looking over the top of her head at the inside of the bar. Then angrily brushing away my cigarette smoke, I answer without looking down at her:

"I don't have any money."

"You never will."

Her strong assertion doesn't move me either. I am alone. The air here isolates you so much that emotions no longer touch you. I glance with indifference at the black hair below my eyes. She continues:

65

"When the winds and the rains awaken young maidens and the earth prepares itself for fertilization, when the rivers of India stir their beds of marvel and mud to purify worshippers, when caravans leave and men think of their bread and their salt, when perfumes climb along the trees to kiss the coming wind, the women of India soften, their lips grow redder, and their eyes get darker. They seek out the mother plant to shade their lovemaking and the sycamore maiden flowers; the sandalwood maiden anoints herself with resin; the violet maiden paints herself with earth; and the willow maiden weaves a hammock of roots on which to celebrate her love. The wind and the rain come. The flowers have already given off their fragrances. Love is hot and humid like the rain in India. That is why the girls strip themselves of their veils, take off their rings, remove their anklets, undo their belts of gold, loosen the nets that hold their hair; they untie the sash of their virginity, they disrobe their bosoms to clothe them with wind and rain, with water and warmth, with humidity and silence. Come, stranger, tonight the wind will blow, the rain will fall, and a violent line will rise upon the horizon. I hear the voice of the mud and of the rivers, and I see the perfume ascend from the flowers."

She has a heavy, unmodulated voice of ritual, a voice of song, a moving, sensual voice. As she speaks, I watch her hands move like the dancers in her country and her feet trace drawings colored in by the dampness.

I fall under the spell of her song. The ritual form of her speech seems to echo precisely something long awaited. I look at her now. She is wearing a Hindu sari, but in this sun, that is not strange even for European women. In her, strangeness is impalpable. It can be found in the bronze but transparent color of her skin, in the obtuse angle of her immense dark eyes, in the fragility of her straight nose, in her obstinate grimace, in the violet and oily blackness of her hair, in the uncontainable movement of her hands with their nails painted in gold -- all blended together with an undefinable Western air that surely does not come from her perfect French or her sense of confidence.

Yes, a strange vapor that seems to come from another world emanates from her. The lyric and ritual tone of her words, on the other hand, still seems perfectly normal to me. Since she has mentioned it, the wind has become a reality. The air no longer feels so heavy and my body, which was sweaty before, has dried within a fresh atmosphere enclosed in the dark atmosphere of the boat, an atmosphere that seems to be able to reach me by my extending my hand a millimeter beyond the area she and I occupied. Then I answer her from within with words so new that they seem to be dictated to me. The extraordinary thing is that I hear myself speak and I agree with what I say:

"I have traveled with the caravans of pilgrims, eating their bread and their salt. My body has been covered with crawling parasites that my skin could not resist. I have slept on the riggings of boats and on the floor of huts. A rich prince invited me to his tent and a prostitute in Singapore shared her mat with me. I search neither for myself nor for others. I have no questions because I belong to

66

everything. I will never be old; my beard will grow dark for many winds and many rains. I have flesh like a tree and while my roots feed on earth my hair caresses the wind. The floor is good for the back, a woman's flesh is warm to the touch, the crust of bread is tender, and the milk is sweet. Therefore I ask you, woman, why do you want me to love you beneath your sycamore?"

That was not my voice or my words. Within me a trace of a Westerner invulnerable to the spell trembled with fear, but all my flesh, my spirit, and my thoughts had changed upon meeting her.

"I was born," she said, "before the rain. When the moonbeam finds the howl of the jackal in the desert. When the animals are thirsty and ripe fruit withers. I was born of a European like you and an Oriental like me. If she had not died taking with her the jackal's cry, my lot would have been different. Neither the waters of the Ganges nor the fur of the she-wolf, nor the red stone would have been able to free me from my fate. But she went away dragging the bad dogs tied to her garments. From then on she treads on them with her sandal so everything flowers for me -- her buds, the scent of her skin, and the milk of her breasts. The bad dogs can bite me only once: in the year that begins after two moons and after that in the year that begins within fourteen moons. My mother chooses her sari for rising, she changes cycle, and for two destinies I will be under the cry of the jackal and my garden will be barren. I left Ceylon by boat to find you, because my nurse, who fed me from her breasts when my mother's dried up, came to see me at the beginning of summer to remind me of the prediction. We burned red beeches together, she bathed me in the river beneath the full moon, she anointed my body and she read, in the blue veins under my arms and the thin wrinkles of my forehead, the voice of my mother, who keeps my jackal in her sari. My mother asks that her sandal be raised within two moons, that I be covered by a white man, like my father, who had blue skin and golden eyes, who tightens the muscles of his jaws, who has red lips, hair on his chest and his back, and an amber star on the palm of his hand between the line of Apollo and the circle of Venus."

When she said this, she took my hand where I saw a fine outline of five points. A shiver of horror shook the Western man in me, while the Oriental one awakened in me by her looked at my marked hand with naturalness and delight.

"Come, stranger, I am goint to intoxicate you."

Then she snapped her fingers covered with rings. As if from nowhere, from the air, a servant appeared.

"Have my musicians come up. Prepare the wine and the fruit. Call the dancers and tell my nurse the guest has arrived. The liquor that flows and the feast that ensues are under your care. Everyone in this boat is my guest, but the stranger, from now on, is your master. Obey him as you do the sound of my bracelets, as I myself obey him."

"Your skin is transparent," I said. "So transparent landscapes can be seen behind it. Look, here is a red cloud that suffocates a flower. Over here a mandrake is born, while over there a star mounts a coral. The wind blows in your flesh. It rains in your glances. Do you know you are beautiful?"

"You speak like men do when a woman listens. We women possess things, they inhabit us; but men see them and feel the need to name them. When things die, when the wind passes, the name that men have given them remains and with them he who cries sweetens his world. Give a name to my skin, to my belly, to my eyes. A name for you; and when we have parted, the words will remain."

"I do not want to part from you."

"But you will be the one to go."

"Then you do not need me for the years of the jackal?"

"I need you. But I do not know if I will be able to hold you back. The element of discord has not yet risen between us, but your Western soul is the thing that will make it come."

I listened to the furious wind and the hurricane-like rain which from that night were to beat upon the boat. Suddenly it seemed absurd for me to be there at her mercy.

"A woman," she said, "can have a man as long as he does not cloak himself in silence. Only his silence is impenetrable."

But I didn't hear her. I was absorbed in my silence. After a considerable amount of time, I returned slowly step by step to reality until I was aware that she was there next to me and pushed from time to time against my side by the movement of the boat. Then I asked:

"You are a queen. Like in the stories from the East, at a wave of your hand, legions of slaves appear who kiss your feet, fulfill your desires, and calm your anger. You must have a slave who combs your hair, another who rubs your transparent skin with perfumed oils, another who disrobes you, and another who puts your sandals on for you. Are you very rich?"

"My mother has already begun to lift her veil. My jackal is going to bite before the second moon."

"Couldn't you speak without metaphors? Couldn't you say something understandable for my Western mind? After all, your father was a Westerner and you know how we speak."

"Yesterday you understood. You will always understand as long as you do not isolate yourself in silence. But if today you do not care to, I am going to speak as you do. I am very rich, so rich that I cannot count all that I have nor calculate the number of sheep in my flock. The trees give fruit for me and the weavers weave with the fibers that come from my fields on looms made of the wood my woodmen cut and with the silk of the cocoons that feed on the mulberry trees in my meadows. I can become poor a hundred times and a hundred times gold will ease my path, for thus it always has been and thus it must always be."

"And you, who know everything, why did you say yesterday that I am always going to be poor?"

"Gold will flee from your hands and everything you touch, except me, will turn wretched. You will never know the color of a ruby, nor will a pearl ever shine in your hand unless it comes from my hand. Whatever you receive from me will wash away immediately as if it were in a river current. But I'll always give you more and more, because I will be rich and you will be poor. That is the way it has been and that is the way it must be."

"If all of your flocks should die and if all of your meadows should become exhausted and if your trees were not to give fruit and if your wheat should dry up on your threshing floors, what would you do?"

"You will see. Tonight we touch at Singapore. You and I will leave the ship without my servants. I want to relieve you of your doubts."

An hour later splendidly dressed in Western attire she was waiting for me. In my threadbare suit, I looked out of place next to her.

"Do you have any money?" she asked.

"This," I said showing her a small coin, "is all I have."

"Give it to me. We will go ashore with this coin alone."

Magic? Sorcery? What should it be called? I almost could not remember the details. I knew that she led me through a strange section of the port. We walked because we didn't have any money. She pressed the little coin in her right hand and with the other hand she held my arm. They tried to stop us at the casino door. Something was said about men in formal attire, but with her commanding voice and a slight gesture, she had the doors opened for us, between two lines of servants bent over at the waist. I told myself that they probably thought it was some mundane whim of the woman or that I was a spy in disguise or who knows what. Anyway, we entered the gambling rooms among the bows and greetings. With the small coin still in her hand, she ordered champagne, music and supper. I trembled but at the same time I had tremendous confidence in the sinister powers of this woman. Then she played.

When the proud little woman put her coin on the table, all eyes turned to her with ironic glances. A dealer told her that such small bets were not permitted. She held to her decision of playing with that coin because her luck depended on it. The dealer bent over and the little noisy ball ran around the roulette wheel. The coin came back to her doubled. Without looking, she placed her bets at random while she drank champagne, gulped down sandwiches, and flirted with me like any woman at Montecarlo or Biarritz. And the coins kept coming back tripled, quadrupled, in heaps, in mountains of glowing gold.

The dealers looked at one another silently and unexpressively. Three hours later the manager came to tell her that she could no longer play because the bank had run out of money.

When we left the casino, she divided the gold. An army of beggars followed us and smilingly she tossed them the coins, which bounced among the crowd. She divided the bills and she tossed them out the car window to the wind. Then she showed me her hand, in which only the original coin remained.

My recollection of what happened next is unclear. Perhaps I was a bit intoxicated or perhaps my Western and French soul was horrified by all that extravagance. Possibly I had spoken biting words to her. She smiled and again a casino's doors were opened for her. Throughout the rest of the night the stacks of gold rose until they almost buried us. The dealers loaded them on the table as if they were grain, and finally, as before, we were told to leave because the bank had exhausted its funds.

On the pier I asked her, "Have you always played? Do you always win?"

"This was the first time I had gone into a casino. That is why I didn't look at the bets, because I didn't know how to place them. But gold will ease my path because that is the way it has been and that is the way it must always be."

Could that bewitching woman turn rain into sunlight? Warm water dense like a veil surrounded the boat, and once again we are sailing in thick waters. You couldn't go out on the deck or walk in the corridors because everything was vibrating, shaking, and swaying. Most of the passengers were in their cabins, seasick, and I, not being so, had been left to my terrifying thoughts. After uselessly shuffling questions and answers back and forth in my head, I went up to look for her. I angrily knocked on her cabin door and from within a voice called out, "Come in."

She was looking at herself very seriously in the mirror in her Hindu dress. When I entered, she didn't move or say anything.

As I walked across the wide cabin, I sank into the rug. I measured the room two, four, sixteen times. She continued looking at herself in the mirror. I had come to explode, to tell her forceful things, to shout at her that it was illegal, dishonest, to manipulate luck as she did. I had come to clarify that I was not willing to be a sheep in her flock, bathed by her river of gold, caressed by her deceitful slave-like words, and dominated by her royal gestures. I had come to shout that I was not willing either to live off her money, to lose my masculine dignity under the pretext that my presence would free her from a legend. I had come to tell her I did not desire her transparent skin, her slanted eyes, her tight lips, or her perfumed flesh.

"A long time ago, before the beginning of time, a man who had had everything in life and had lost it all was crying over his past. He had been handsome, rich, kind. Great people used to go to him to take part in his serenity and the humble ones to share his happiness. His women put on his sandals after kissing his feet. His beautiful children used to listen to his words and learn them to repeat them later to their children. This wise man had the joy of the birds and the peace of the sand. But he lost everything, and that is why he was crying seated at the edge of the road without his tranquility and joy, his bread and wine, his wife and child. And then he heard a song. He stopped crying for a second and waited. At the end of the path, a beggar, who was almost dragging himself, approached. He was old. His tearful eyes revealed the yellow undersides of his eyelids; parasites swarmed his ragged clothes; his empty bundle had no bread. When he had passed, the sad man who had lost everything except his wisdom, asked himself this question: If this beggar sings, tell me why you, who have such beautiful memories, are crying?"

She paused, turned toward me, and added:

"Don't destroy what later will be your only richness. Always make sure that today's memory does not darken your tomorrow. You are angry, and like the wind in the desert, you do not know what route to take, so you shake the sand, darken the air, chill the breeze, disturb the landscape. Listen to me, stranger, I am going to answer the question you do not dare to ask."

And again, like the afternoon I met her, she took on a ritual, monotonous, caressing voice to tell me:

"The face of the moon hasn't changed since I met you, but your face has shown love, voluptuousness, anger, disenchantment, and even fear. You Westerners have many faces. Passions pass through our Eastern souls without upsetting them. Disenchantment is as deep as the water in a well. Voluptuousness is only an aroma, love runs like the subterranean rivers that nurture the oases, and fear only strikes the body, the flesh, all that is transitory, but never the spirit. What do you fear, stranger and master of this woman?"

Once again, like the first time and contrary to my will, I spoke in symbols with words unknown to me:

"A few nights ago, before the rain, you invoked the jackals of your destiny with the amber star of my hand. Afterwards we saw in my questions and my rebellion your mother's sandal lifting before the second moon and the bad dogs began to howl. If I have the water of your gardens locked in me and if your wolves will jump upon my waist without biting me, why must my fortune be in your hands? Why can't I conjure your destiny and why can't you free me of your sandal? Why must I be subject to your power? If I must always be poor, let me continue on my pilgrim journey and you continue on your road of queen."

She lowered her head to answer me:

"We women do not love in order to possess a man. We want to belong to his tent, to sleep on his rug, to tie his sandals, and to hold his horse's bridle before he goes away. We do not want to receive but to be received. The important part of a relationship with a man is not to say 'this man is mine.' Women never have had a cabin, a well, fields, or wheat. They are the cabin, the well, the fields, the wheat. I will be the hand of my lord, his whip, the gesture with which he caresses, the wind that carries him off, and the voice with which he bids me farewell. There is little difference between you and me. To separate us would be like separating skin from flesh. I cannot make gold rise from your feet and make good fortune pave your path. But I am your foot and below that foot cattle will grow, fruit will ripen, the trees of the forest will fall and wheat will become golden. You, on the other hand, will walk with me during the years of the jackal. Only you can bring about the prediction. The amber star in your hand is the safeguard that my mother has put in you for when she, in two moons and until the fourteenth moon, raises her sari and frees the evil dogs, which, without you, will bite me."

All my European and masculine rebellion came out in this answer:

"But I will depend on you, I will live and eat from your hand, I will be protected by your sari. That cannot be."

"You, master, command my will, you live in my blood. The fourteen moons of my death become life in you. Say that you will have me and my mother will smile in her dwelling."

After these words I was only aware of her transparent skin, of the violet fragrance that lingered on her breast, and of the honey of her sleepy eyes.

As I looked at Hong Kong before me the form of my escape grew. I had to escape like a thief, climbing down the boat cables. I fell into the water and swam aimlessly in a sea strewn with rubbish from the port, avoiding the vision of the boats and the watchful eyes of the fishermen. Later I loaded bundles on the dock to earn a few cents. I ate rice and drank some rum in a tavern; I slept with a prostitute to suppress my memories; and now here I am in a low class hotel, tired, within an exhausted body that asks me to lie down and with an alert spirit that doesn't let me sleep. From the window I can see the water lapping against the sea wall. A jungle of shouts rises from the street below; the boats blink in the distance; and one of them must be the one that is carrying her. After all, as a civilized person I cannot succumb to the strange sorcery of a woman who puts words in my mouth, caresses in my hand, glances in my eyes, and, above all, gold at my feet. I regain my alert conscience. My masculine logic returns. Orderly thoughts flower in my mind and the metaphors and symbols disappear with the boat in the blinking immensity.

I think such rational things as, "I must forget." Then I divide myself in two and to console myself, I blame the half that is no longer, because it went with her, for all that I did. I have woken up. I am once again a European in Asia with an adventurer's route, without money and without hope, who will travel with the caravans and who will share his rice with a pilgrim to be able some day to recount it all with the nostalgic tone of an old sailor. Among my stories there will be one that begins like this: "When the winds and rains awaken the maidens, when the rivers of India stir their beds of marvels and mud to purify worshippers. . ." Any of my listeners will want to have lived the magical story to which time will add details and my memory will subtract symbols.

Now I return to my body. And thinking about it, I stretch out in the dirty bed, which is surely full of many parasites, because for four cents you can't find a clean bed in Hong Kong or anywhere else. I don't feel the insects because my fatigue is such that sleep begins to turn my thoughts into lines and squares. I know that when things lose their verbal form and become figures, I am about to fall asleep. This is so natural that no matter how strange the visions, brilliant the color, and fast the movement, their appearance in my unconscious produces a consoling sense of rest in me. But this time before the forms take shape and the colors are defined, the incredible heaviness of my body disappears and I awake. I jump out of bed and with great horror, I realize that I have not moved a muscle. I am stretched out, face up like before. I feel my heart beating, my blood circulating, my nerves vibrating. I feel that my cells are devouring one another and that although many processes are going on as normal, I am not in control of my body. I think of catalepsis. An alive spirit but an inert, dead body in which respiration isn't even visible. Men who are buried alive without being able to defend themselves because they are not masters of their organism. I must be sweating because the painful and fruitless effort to move exhausts my energy, but I know I am motionless. I think about my foot so far away from my head; I think about my eyes and I move my eyelids, but nothing happens to them. I look for my voice, the voice with which a pursued man or one who is drowning shouts. As an answer I make out the tick-tock of the clock, the jungle of shouts in the street, and the noise of the tide. And then my hand begins to move. It's my hand, but it isn't because I didn't intend or try to move it. I have thought about my foot and my eye, but not about my hand. I try to lower it, but my hand continues rising slowly against my will. It moves up my belly and along my skin without moving its fingers or the clothing. I can't do anything to stop my hand. It is so strong that I know without a doubt it has all the power in the world. It can stop a mountain from falling and without violence; that hand of mine and someone else's can uproot a tree completely. My hand goes up, and inside myself I shout for help; I reach an animal-like panic, I struggle, I defend myself against my hand. But my body no longer belongs to me. My hand has reached my chest, and I finally understand what it wants: to strangle me! If my hand can change the course of a river and can knock down a cliff in a single blow, then it will find the defenseless flesh of my body, it will break the bones of my back, and it will make me die uprooted like a tree. My hand is already moving slowly along my chest. My terror has pushed me nearly to the point of fainting. Perhaps when it all happens I won't feel anything because I will have lost consciousness. My hand goes up, and finally I shout. A beastly incomparable shouting that makes all my veins stand out and opens my pores so that cold sweat can run through them like interminable rivers.

I manage to stop myself and I go over to the window. I must flee from this place too; I have to find refuge from her. But my legs tremble; the guilty hand hangs at my side with an amber star in its palm. I am so frightened that to leave or run or shout would be all the same. The tide has reached its maximum; the waves consume each other and eat away on the sea wall. They pant among the piles of the dock, cry in the riggings of the moored boats, and sing a hoarse chorus against the keels of the anchored boats. A little later, calmer now, I manage to go down the stairs and lose myself in the street, among the people, feeling defended by them.

I have spent the rest of the night drinking. I don't understand how I didn't fall asleep standing up or how I was able to lift sacks on the docks in the morning. I earned a few more cents, ate rice and went to find a prostitute to have some company but I couldn't find one. Everyone seems strange to me. I am afraid. Nevertheless, my fatigue is so great that almost without realizing it, I am again stretched out on the dirty bed and once again the colored forms fill my mind. I know I am going to go to sleep.

I hear the sound of the waves. The tide returns at night. "I was born," she said, "when the moon beam finds the howl of the jackal in the desert." You could see landscapes through her olive skin and flocks of sheep grazed in her sleepy eyes. She will be my cabin, my well, my field, and my wheat. Today my dreams have the form of a sycamore, and when death comes, they will crown me with fragrant flowers. I am beginning to enter unconsciousness; ceasing to be, I will find rest. When I move to turn on my side as I always do to fall asleep, like yesterday, my body does not respond to the movement. I shout without words, I struggle again without gestures, I shiver without convulsions, and I drown. My hand, the hand that would uproot a tree, begins to rise, and like last night, it goes up my stomach and across my chest to reach my neck. I am going to die. I am going to assassinate myself. The thought of it seems strange but I have nothing with which to resist it. My own powerful hand is going to kill me. I succumb to it and strong resignation fills my conscience.

Is it her hand or mine that is going to kill me? It is hers. To be killed by her, who held the wind slave to her word, is not strange. She, who heard all that ears do not hear and eyes do not see, can also implacably cause death. And I thought I held the water of her gardens and controlled the jackals in my waist! And now I am going to die by my hand not hers! Again I hear the tide striking and eating away at the sea wall, lapping the dock, scratching the keels, and panting among the riggings. I no longer try to shout. My hand goes up, up, up. If I could move my head, I would lift it in order to see how my hand is assassinating me, not to stop it, because that was written in her gazelle eyes and I, who dreamt once about stopping the jackals that are going to devour her in fourteen moons, cannot do anything against this hand now hers. My hand goes up passing along my neck. It goes up. . .

And then I feel that with transparent olive skin that smells like violets and tastes like honey, my hand is caressing the contours of my mouth, stopping sweetly at its corners, and passing, like a delicate breeze, along its surface. The gesture is sweet, loving, profound. Then while my eyes cry and all my muscles relax, my hand goes down to its customary place, it stretches out innocently, and from the boat that no longer blinks in the distance, these words reach me:

"I will be my master's hand, his whip, the gesture with which he caresses, the wind that carries him off, and the voice with which he bids me farewell."

Reality in the Fiction of "High Valley"

by Victoria Urbano
Translated by Vivian Gruber

"High Valley" belongs to the so-called Mexican cycle of Yolanda Oreamuno's stories, because it takes place in Mexico. Its theme, however, is universal. The anonymous characters are individuals who meet by chance and the narration focuses on their encounter which happens without deliberate intent. It is just like a halt in the road, free of tragedy, sanctions or morals.

The total absence of identifying elements diffuses the importance of the characters and envelopes them in an atmosphere of laxity. On the other hand, a certain mystery within their apparent human simplicity is emphasized.

The lack of names contributes to making the events more natural, with no individualized consequences. Nothing there seems to have a finality. Time passes as a monotonous succession never arriving at a precise climax.

With such a simple, elemental and unintriguing plot, the interest of the reader is maintained because the author knows how to apply the same procedure to the real world that she is using in the fictitious one. Bit by bit, as if by chance, both the reader and the protagonist of "High Valley" are exposed to main details. The mystery unfolds smoothly, naturally. Nothing is planned with the intention of suspense. By this double process of creating within and outside the story, Yolanda revealed her art and genius. By work of magic, she transforms the reader into an actor, who, together with the protagonist, continues the journey and the exploration into the human geography of the characters.

Yolanda's technique derived from her urgency to manifest her own position before life, by which she created circumstances and attitudes similar to those she was familiar with or for which she experienced a very personal interest. Intuitively, almost as in the recondite symbolism of poetry where the artist empties his whole being, scrutinizing and revealing himself, Yolanda wrote her works. She used her own creations to demonstrate a point of view, a sentiment, a desire; or to criticize a norm, an idea, a prejudice; or to unburden an anguish; or to affirm a personality, a mood or spiritual state. No matter what, she always had something personal to say and that was her most urgent and important reason for writing "High Valley" and everything else.

Her frank and uninhibited letters serve to clarify the behaviour, surrenders or inevitable deceptions of her characters. They also help to understand the hidden mysteries and symbols which went from real suffering in her personal life to creation. She said in one of her letters:

"Always my dreams will be greater than reality."

"Always my surrender will surpass that of anyone else and I ask for a like surrender which I never find nor shall I ever find. I must confine myself to seeing my adventure without hope. The marvelous part of that adventure is not in what is discovered, but in the journey itself to seek it. Each man must be for me as a continent of magic that I create, no matter how mediocre he may be. I must remain with my dream, with my thirst of dangerous lands found inside each individual and I must live only for this search. Otherwise I rot away in the tremendous solitude which I endure so badly, and which comes up when I renounce the luxury of these dreams."[1]

Now we can understand why the male character of "High Valley" has only the importance of being a new man in the life of the protagonist; as such, he becomes a motive of dream and hope, no matter how mediocre he is, because her imagination has already changed him into a continent of magic. The adventure, however, is hopeless. With a meaningful choice of words, Yolanda stated that the protagonist "resignedly had accepted everything that was to come" because all dreams end in abandonment.

Among the symbols of "High Valley", wind-man-rain are equivalent. The drought under the exhausting heat corresponds to the anguish of a lonely woman. For this reason, the male character addressing his companion tells her: "It's going to rain, baby. You'll be soaked and I shall do nothing to prevent it because I want to see the water run from your hair, down your cheeks and into the deep corners of your mouth." "Look how the rain is already beating down on the hills. The pasture lands will drink up the moisture, and I shall drink it in your face. This is the final struggle. It comes winning, victorious, to calm the great longing. If this were to continue forever, you and I also would wait forever."[2]

Thus, when the storm and the trip end, wind, rain and man disappear. The protagonist will keep on discovering "the island of her own agony and the mountains of men's stupidity." Her search is pure nostalgia of origin. Rather than love of man, it is fear of loneliness that impels her to continue searching. But all is hopeless.

-----

[1]Urbano, Victoria, **Una escritora costarricense: Yolanda Oreamuno**, p. 133

[2]See P. 62 in this book.

"The Tide Returns at Night"

by Yolanda Oreamuno
Catherine G. Bellver

Yolanda Oreamuno weaves in her "The Tide Returns at Night" ("Las mareas vuelven de noche") an intriguing fantasy, a disturbing dream, and an ambivalent world in which exterior reality is transposed, with the aid of the author's sensitive imagination, into a poetic experience. The elements of legend and the presence of superhuman powers are intensified and elaborated by Oreamuno's choice of structure, by her characterization, or more exactly her lack of psychological penetration, and by her conscious use of language.

An unidentified European meets an enigmatic Indian woman aboard a ship in Hong Kong harbor. Her mysterious attraction overwhelms the man. In fulfillment of her destiny she must lie with a white man like her father to loosen the cry of the jackals and free herself. Her salvation depends on the man's submission to her magic powers. Although surrender to her will bring no pain but sexual pleasure and riches, the man cannot consent to the forfeiture of his masculine independence. Even though the Eastern woman contends that women do not want to receive but to be received, that they never have possessions but are themselves man's possession, her alluring and exotic powers cast a disturbing spell upon the European. He struggles not to become a passive receiver of her dominion and passion while contradictory forces propel him toward involuntary self-destruction. He attempts to escape the strange sorcery of this strange woman by leaving the boat, but obsessive memories of the woman with the transparent olive skin turn into a nightmarish struggle with death at her hand -- or his, both of which have become one in her sexual surrender to him. Unlike the Oriental fable, Oreamuno's story illustrates no moral, and unlike modern surrealist literature it shows no penetration into the human psyche. It merely exposes the interplay and conflict between two vital expressions of the vital force of corporal desire.

Although set in the Orient, in Hong Kong harbor, the city itself and the world of exterior reality are incidental in the story. We the readers are conscious of the existence of Hong Kong and we are provided with a fleeting glimpse of the port when the two protagonists disembark, but the real world remains essentially a diaphanous and irrelevant backdrop which serves as a tenuous structure for the action without coming to life as a concrete, conscientiously defined or truly existing world. Far from wanting to photograph an exotic environment, Oreamuno attempts to create a universal, generalized scene that transcends all localization and complements her equally generalized characters.

The anonymity of her two central characters helps to remove them from the real world and to deprive each of a human identity. Although the Indian

77

woman relates her story with special insistence and the author provides ample description of her (heavy enchanting voice, bronze transparent skin, immense dark eyes, fragile nose, violet black hair, gold nails, and enticing scent), she remains an apparition, never becoming a woman of flesh and blood. Even her magic dominion and her sexual attraction never descend from the heights of sorcery and myth. She stands draped in beauty and intrigue as a mystifying force but never reveals the presence of a human personality.

Although the male protagonist exhibits his humanity in his struggle to maintain his personal liberty and integrity, he is never identified by name, personal background, or specific distinguishing circumstances. He seems to embody a struggle with destiny more than experiencing it; he seems to represent psychological disorientation more than containing it. He, like the Indian woman, are to the end creations and not creatures.

In "The Tide Returns at Night" there prevails a thick atmosphere and a dense style that depends on suggestive elements burdened with sensory images and poetic figures. From the initial images of water thickened to the consistency of oil and of humid, dark air to the final image of the ambivalent hand of destruction, the vividness of the imagery establishes a striking antagonism with the dream-like situation and the aura of mystery that pervade the entire tale.

The lush description helps to clothe the tale in a mantle of fantasy. The story the girl tells and the highly subjective portrait of her that the author paints make for a very unreal being, reminiscent of the princesses of Eastern fables or of the maidens from the Arabian nights. But unlike the damsels of the secret gardens and idyllic paradises of these fables, we are never convinced, even for one moment, of the reality of Oreamuno's creation. Her story remains a vision for us, the readers, for her unfortunate protagonist, and perhaps also for herself.

Haunting repetitions within the same sentence or as echoes throughout the story create a throbbing musicality as well as suggesting a chant for the underlying atmosphere of sorcery. The closing lines of the composition are, in fact, in their reiteration, a fulfillment of the prophecy uttered by the woman of the olive complexion and the scent of violets.

The abrupt transitions from description to dialogue to interior monologue and the intermingling of present action with open reflections upon past occurrences only serve to heighten the general sensation of mystery and enigma. The emotional climate builds throughout the story from dream to nightmare, closing in a scene of intense hysteria in which all distinction between fantasy and reality, between the man and the woman, between time and its fame, here and there are obliterated. The conscious creation of ambivalence in the work reaches its fruitful climax and conclusion in the murderous hand which, as ultimate evidence of the fusion and confusion of different forces, belongs neither to him nor to her, but becomes "mi mano suya."

4

VICTORIA URBANO

VICTORIA URBANO

Born in Costa Rica in 1926 and, after beginning in early childhood to show a marked inclination for poetry and writing, she has continued to follow her natural vocation at a prolific pace.

With the creation of **RITMO** she produced the first student newspaper of the Colegio Superior de Señoritas as a teenager in San José. Then, in 1945, she went to San Francisco, California to study English and business. By 1951, her first book of short stories, **MARFIL**, was published and she had become very active in the Golden Gate city writing for several newspapers, giving television recitals and presiding over Círculo Hispanoamericano and its prominent lecture series.

Nineteen Hundred and Fifty-two saw her enrolling in Spain's Royal Conservatory of Dramatic Arts where she later graduated with honors. Two of her plays were, at that time, produced in Madrid with excellent reviews for skill in dramatic writing. In 1960, she entered the University of Madrid where she obtained her M.A. and Ph.D., Magna Cum Laude.

Returning to the States in 1966 to teach Spanish at Lamar University, Beaumont, Texas, she was awarded the life title of Regents' Professor in recognition of her outstanding teaching and research activities in 1972.

Recipient of many international honors and prizes, she has, among others: the Silver Medal "Dr. José Arce" of Argentina, the Ribbon of Honor of Spain, the title of Vice-Consul of Costa Rica, the International Prize for Literature, "León Felipe 1969" for her book of short stories **Y era otra vez hoy**, "Premio Cultura Hispánica" on History for her book **Juan Vázquez de Coronado**, and the International Prize for Poetry "Fray Luis de León" for her book, **Los Nueve Círculos**. She has also received seven research awards and many other academic honors which have been listed in more than 15 international biographic collections having to do with literary research and poetry, as well as having been included in many anthologies of poetry and short stories.

She has published 12 books, more than 200 articles, and has numerous works yet unpublished. Some of her published books are:

Marfil (Ediciones Botas, Mexico 1951- short stories and poetry)
La niña de los caracoles (Madrid, Spain 1961, prose)
Platero y tú (Col. Orosí, Madrid 1962. prose)
Juan Vázquez de Coronado y su ética en la conquista de Cosa Rica (Ediciones Cultura Hispánica, Madrid, 1968 - History)
Una escritora costarricense: Yolanda Oreamuno (Ediciones Castilla de Oro, Madrid 1968, estudio literario)
Los Nueve Círculos (Ediciones Castilla de Oro, Madrid, 1972, poetry)
El teatro español y sus directrices contemporáneas (Editora Nacional, Madrid 1973)
Y era otra vez hoy (Premio "León Felipe", Finisterre, Editor, Mexico 1972, short story)
El Teatro en Centroamérica, desde sus orígenes hasta 1975 (EDUCA, Costa Rica 1978)
Agar, la esclava (Teatro Bellas Artes, Madrid, 1952 - Play)
La hija de Charles Green (Teatro de Cultura Hispánica, Madrid, 1954 - Play)
Freeway to Italian (Lamar University Press, Beaumont, Texas 1977 - Grammar)

AVERY ISLAND

Victoria Urbano
Translated by Katharine C. Richards

I should be able to find the grove of giant bamboo. While the road is dusty and the afternoon explodes with heat, the grove I seek will be cool and shady, perpendicular, opaque, enveloped in the yellow-green of the canes.

Stagnant water. Swamp slime. Enormous algae clusters mingle with a net of bulbs and roots to scratch the corrugated backs of crocodiles. Where can they be? Above the slippery green of the swamp, bamboo scaffolds hold up the white curve of twenty thousand flamingos, a feathered island of beauty.

The crocodiles, their eyelids puffy and their jaws lined with an army of bayonets, roam the swamp and slide beneath the dirty green water, the surface is left trembling, wrinkled from anxiety and treachery.

Beneath the flaming sun, the serenity of the flamingos looks like a snow-covered lake as they tend twenty thousand newly-hatched lives.

Where is it? Where is the bamboo grove? Over there, beyond the azalea garden after you cross the avenue of oaks, an arrow points left.

What a strange sight they are, these huge trees with their hanging parasites, foreboding and romantic!

Edgar Allan Poe. Echo and solitude. As though the trees had rent their clothing of silence and then covered themselves with rags and wild strands of hair. If the moving waves of the sea were to turn to stone penetrated by the wind, they would be like the parasitic hair on these ancient oaks and Edgar Allan Poe would be able to hear his laments echoing from tree to tree: "Anabel Lee. . ."

But where is it? Where is the bamboo grove? The dust and heat weigh on my eyelids and my lashes. Like sand on my finger tips, it clings to my dry, brown body.

Up there, if you follow the road marked by the arrow, is the pagoda. The Buddha is young, smiling, beardless, a poet dreaming among bamboo whispers. He has slender shoulders and beautiful hands -- and a stomach that has not yet become grotesque. He lives in a world of crystal and bamboo.

There is no sound of splashing fountains, no sound of flowing water. The lilies and ducks float like paper boats on motionless water.

Here, at this boulder, the path descends toward the green coolness of the woods. Yes, I hear now the languid sound of plumed headdresses thrusting aside the clouds. It is the huge canes, stretching to the height of the pagoda on the hill, where they meet the gaze of the poet as he dreams in his world of crystal.

The road narrows, tunnel-like. It is confined by voices, music, forests of independent notes. Birds, leaves, or is it my ears? Perhaps, it is myself that I begin to hear. The universe is rhythm, music, sound. Everything else is onomatopoeia. Thought and language.

Now, I can feel the cool. Tightly packed and wet, the earth lies beneath the stone. On either side tropical plants stick out their sharp tongues and make my flesh crawl. The mosquitoes suck human blood delightedly, unaware that they will die poisoned by sadness or diabetic lust.

What is that black butterfly doing as it flies among the sinuous ferns? It must be startled by my presence, my thought, the strange heat of my arms as I pass through the shadowy cool created by the plants.

Now, I see them, the bamboo stalks. Before my eyes a world of rings and lances. How could anyone say that woods are solitary? A thousand giant legs rise above my head. Where are the torsos of their bodies? Is it possible that I am afraid to enter, to press on fleeing from the heat, to find myself alone in my own company? I hear footsteps behind me. No, it is only the dull tread of my feet, traveling along the sensitive canes and sounding like distant echoes. Above the dark moist earth here and there the canes shine like straw. The Egyptians' legs must have been like that, Ramses II and Osiris stretching up into the sky.

Is someone following me?

A dead bamboo -- it was an arrow once -- lies arched in baroque contrast to the vertical life of the others.

Why am I quickening my pace? I should see and observe this bamboo world, where I find coolness and shadows intensified each time I enter. Now and then, shafts of sunlight penetrate vertically like mature canes. As I hurry, I seem to be immobile, because it is the naked bamboo legs that move, hurry, run. Not I.

Why am I running? The contrasting light and shadow impart movement to the giants. "Rashomon." I remember the movie, for it impressed me deeply Someone fleeing through a forest, feet, light and shadows.

Is someone chasing me? Where is it, where is the way out? These huge canes. Is it possible that bamboo can be this thick? I had never noticed the roots before, strings joining the stalks to the ground with coarse stitches. Some of the canes bend under their own weight and interlace to form gothic naves, but what affects me most is the nakedness of this dense grove.

Velazquez. Yes, there, in that rectangle of light framed in green, I can see the painting of the spears, **The Surrender of Breda**.

What barbarous hand cut down this stalk? I need to continue on the same narrow path so as not to lose my way. What would happen if night were to fall suddenly here in the bamboo grove? Where is the way out? I've lost the trail. It wasn't here. . .Footsteps. Yes, I hear them. They are not echoes this time, for my feet are still. Under them, the earth is starting to feel cool. Did I take off my sandals without realizing it? Yes, and I cannot move. Cords as thin as nerves have stitched my feet tightly and securely to the earth, and someone is coming. The sound of footsteps echoes in the distance and the canes, responsive to the sounds, carry them to my ear. In the clearings, the windows of light are getting dark. Motionless, I begin to see in the shadows shapes created by my imagination.

At night, feet are imprisoned by the bamboo. They kick off their sandals, and the tall canes become transformed into serpents.

"Why serpents?"

"Because, now that I think about it, a bamboo has vertebrae and, when it is erect like this, it must be a cobra hypnotized by the Buddha there on the hilltop."

"Childish nonsense!"

"Or, the canes will become crocodiles and come to eat me."

"What pretentiousness! As if you were a flamingo!"

"You may be right. Maybe it is conceit, but I tell you I can feel my soul, splendid and white, when I dream. Today after seeing the flamingos, I am sure that my soul is an island of feathered beauty like them."

"You're dreaming again. Wake up. Try to find your way out."

"Why? Outside the grove, it will be hot."

"Shh. Be quiet and listen. Do you hear steps?"

"Yes. It is the approach of night."

"No it's not the night. It is he that is coming toward me now."

High above the platforms of giant bamboo the moon is making its nest. A thousand beaks of light burst chirping upon the heavens.

I hear steps. Yes, it is solitude approaching.

Sweet, sad? What is solitude like?

Vast and serene, like the gaze of the poet in his crystal world.

It is he. The Buddha from the hilltop is coming.

His smile is serene, his skin aglow in greenish light as the moon filters through the bamboo.

I cannot move. My feet have grown roots. My legs have grown long and thin while my body reaches upward toward the night. I am tied to the earth, but my memories, presentiments, stray thoughts and solitude are free like long locks of hair. It's like being one of the bamboo. A strange feeling. Sixteen years ago I had a similar sense of reintegration with the earth. From time to time we go beyond ourselves, go through ourselves in cycles, and encounter our being anew, there where we found it first.

The Buddha pauses beside a cane and speaks to it. His words are imbued with music. No, there are no words. His voice is pure music.

The dark, moist earth trembles beneath my feet, and I feel the plants loosening their braided roots below it. The bamboos, so straight, so still, are transformed before my eyes into human figures; their arms separate, shed their rings, encircle the waist of the moonlit night. I, who once was soul, arms and legs in a dream, only I remain bound to the earth, like the sigh of a tree. I find myself changing while he, with arms extended, comes toward me.

The boughs that were my shoulders are weighed down by the strange sensation of having lived in other centuries, of being myself no longer, as I stand here motionless but astir with feeling, moved by the vast, naked emotion of the bamboo grove.

I remember. Oh yes, I remember the villa Borghese. I was enraptured, contemplating the incredible Bernini sculpture, Apollo's abduction of Daphne, and I felt the force of unfulfilled yearning, the embrace withheld, love transformed into laurel... Suddenly, I was alone, lost in a white sea of nostalgia and beauty. I closed my eyes. When I opened them I encountered his gaze upon me. Beneath the marble moon his olive skin looked darker and more intense.

The poet from a world of crystal and bamboo comes toward me. He looks at me anxiously as if afraid I might turn to foliage, beyond his reach. His insistent gaze, rests upon my long-fingered hands. Momentarily, his eyes half-close, and the darkness of the grove grows deep and solemn. Then the moon shines forth anew amid the olive-green clouds.

Yes, I remember. I had stopped to look at the reclining nude of Pauline Bonaparte, and under the spell of that moonlike marble, I had the feeling of having lived in other centuries, of being myself no longer, as I stood there, motionless and astir with feeling in the vast nakedness of Art.

I am bound to the earth like the sigh of a tree. And before my eyes the metamorphosis of night takes place. An ant scurries across my body. Where is the poet? I want his golden voice to dissipate the witches' Sabbath in the shadows.

Three female figures approach, their faces hidden beneath their long locks of hair. They clasp each other by their bare shoulders, like three languid graces. They kneel before me and loosen the invisible cords that tie my feet to the ground. A strange feeling of freedom rises through my legs. The three, dressed in white moonlight, lead me even further into the grove. One of them stands still and prepares to sacrifice a frog, croaking in its leafy hiding place. It is a young frog, soft green in color with black spots. The woman spreads its lower extremities, then presses them against its white belly to empty the bladder. Her two companions, wearing surgical masks, prepare a knife, tweezers and scalpel. The grove has turned into a mysterious laboratory with tables and apparatus I do not recognize. They insert the scalpel into the frog's head and destroy its brain. Its eyes are opened incredibly wide, staring at my terror. The phantom nurses affix him to a cork slab, begin cutting the skin at the extremities, and lift it to reveal a gelatinous, naked mass of nerves and muscles. They open the thorax and the small heart beats rhythmically with a life I cannot understand. I cannot look away from his unwavering stare. Cold drops of sweat dampen my forehead and my upper lip. My finger tips are alarmingly cold, and I nearly faint from sudden weakness. They seize the heart with tweezers attached by a thread to a smoke-black cylinder. The continued beating marks a perfect diagram, peaks and dips alternating harmoniously on the cylinder. Is this what life is? Where, oh where, is the beauty of the twenty thousand flamingos? And why is there no expression in the eyes of the poor, sacrificed animal? Where are the moon marble sculptures carved by the capricious light? Where is my voice hiding? A wall of silence stifles my inner cry and my anguish lies broken in a thousand pieces, transformed into pathetic faces. Every shadow, every leaf grimaces with pain, the silent pain of the little frog, whose heart continues to beat while his eyes stare fixedly at my terror. In those dilated pupils that are my mirror, I see Goya's ambiguous, disconcerting picture of the old men supping. The lewd laughter of the witches slides harshly over the frog's bloody skull, and images of life turn to images of death in the open, paradoxical drama of existence. On the smoky cylinder, the needle continues to trace its curve of peaks and dips while the moon, in the tragic night that follows the silent insurrection, becomes a monstruous lamp shining into the senseless iris of the frog. In the uncertain light everything around me is transformed into a demon world that defies and questions. The bamboo grove has turned into the black magic of Goya's witches, and the approaching Buddha, who used to be a poet in a mansion of crystal and whispers, has become a devil, disguised as a male goat, symbol of the negative powers that unsettle human existence. Where, oh where, has the beauty gone? I am aware only of intense panic growing within me and reflected in the frog's staring eyes. Where is the beauty, the resplendent color of the **Naked Maja**? The entire grove is a black escutcheon registering the rhythmic beating of a palpitating heart. The blood from the animal's skull takes hold of the intimate structure of my silent language. My fingers, alarmingly frozen, obey a tragic impulse and dip into the blood. The dramatic sight of those stained fingernails. Once more, Goya comes to mind, the vivid scene of **The Fight with Clubs** that he painted on the walls of the "House of the Deaf Man." I see the two men, their legs buried in mud, their faces bloodied, fighting desperately. All the bamboo canes, formerly slender and beautiful like airy, feather headdresses, have turned into a heap of drunken madmen as night descends despairingly over the plateau of tragic human destiny.

I place my hands against my heart and feel it beat with the intensity of a volcanic eruption, burning desperation and the passionate desire for mercy. Can this be life or is it rather an atrocious nightmare that I see through the eyes of a sacrificed animal? Where, oh where, is the immeasurable, profound beauty of life? Why this absurd sequence of fantastic, terrifying scenes, the dark side of soaring imagination? Can it be a desperate attempt to flee? The frog stares fixedly upon my terror. The mirror of his dilated pupils holds me strangely spell-bound. They stir the ambiguity and the absurdity of my own being.

The Buddha of a thousand reveries, changed into a devil in Buddha form, now appears dressed in white like the ghostly nurses, stitching the rhythm of the beating heart. With a pair of open scissors, he advances and severs the thread of life. A doubtful act. Was it inspired by pity or deviltry?

The Goyesque visions, strange preludes of myself, preludes of the existential anguish which governs human events, attain their terrifying violence in an ancient myth. And, the Devil-Buddha, the cutter of life, transformed anew, seizes the frog and devours it before my eyes like a disheveled, terrifying Saturn, like time destroying its children. Cold perspiration moistens my forehead and I fall upon the damp earth of the grove. The bamboo legs, that used to be slender and agile, follow the Buddha like a crawling human flock carrying sacks of illusion, superstition and sadness on their backs.

Where, where is happiness? Magical color is forming its hues softly around me. Once again I feel like the sigh of a tree upon the earth.

II

Once again I feel like the sigh of a tree upon the earth.

A faint melancholy trembles in the distant waning light. I stand on the shores of a fantastic lake of memories. Vibrant colors fill me with happiness and peace tinted with shades of yellow, while the light blue depths of the surrounding air show me their transparent palaces. Is this a different song of life? Perhaps happiness is autumn, pure colors that charm the eye. Strange, inverted counterpoint. . .human melancholy, like a vermilion stain, serves to accentuate the lovely green of joy. Sweet, luminous portrait of my soul. This grove is an extraordinary gallery of persons recreated from my inner, secret self. This mysterious assembly of trees is an open hymn of youth sounding in my ears. Happiness is a river that barely lasts a minute. It comes, draws near, passes through me and is mine no longer. It departs and with it takes the scent of my smile in its crystalline transparency. Happiness, is it given to me or do I take it for myself? Do I steal it or is it stolen from me? I know it yet it is never mine. Or perhaps it is mine and I know it not.

The coolness of the earth makes me begin to shiver. Its cold scissors lift my skin and make me aware of the naked gelatinous knot of nerves and muscles within me. Silken tweezers pinch my heart. I hear it beating, and in the shadows of twilight its rhythm sketches the images of my memories.

The twilight shadows are a meadow of violets.

The palace at Aranjuez. High grass, fountains, fauns and Apollos, intimate gardens with their unfailing murmur of water. Leaves and, under them, a small flower, trembling in extreme modesty while my shameless toes uncover its beauty. You told me once that my feet were as delicate as a statue's and ever since I've gratified my vanity by looking at my bare feet as I place them on the back of the earth. Is this happiness? Aranjuez but Avila, as well, with its austere landscape, monastic, penitent. Not violets, but stones beneath a diamond sky. There, like one more mystic, my bare feet traversed the fortress of God.

Violets and stone. The Good Friday procession with the great baroque images filled me with emotion. Amid the prayers and solemn sounds I felt my world to be brimming with passions. All of this was Spain, a country of convoluted contrasts, and deep down inside me, a drop of happiness that was a still, dilated pupil, mirror of a microcosm, where geraniums, lemons and the lime mineral symbolized my origin. I had not been born there, but I had made it mine, had been reborn -- out of caprice, will and freedom because through my desire to do it, alone and through my will, I had molded circumstance, destiny, caprice and will, which life imposes. And, willing it, I could do it. Was this the procession of penitents passing before me, the ones who lash themselves on their bare backs to find pleasure in their pain? Happiness is only a word which has come into the possession of our anguish. Anguish is a whip we use to make us bleed from pleasure. Happiness exists in that realm where we have it not, and it is in looking for it that we are happy sometimes. And if we find it? We must not touch, must not imprison it, must not make it our own, because that would mean losing it forever. Happiness is not one reality, but many. It is given us in bits and pieces that are fragmented like a landscape, which can only be approached from various angles and never with a single look.

Spain, but also Rio. When you take the cable car to the Christ on Corcovado, the smell of the tropical jungle is not warm. It is impenetrably cool. Cords of parasitic plants anxiously seek the sky, but as they climb up the trees they become entangled so that they never reach the goal. High above, where man is small beside the gigantic statue of Christ, the disproportion seems miraculous. The soul grows larger in contemplation of the panoramic grandeur spread out before the eye.

The great Christ of stone appeared small to me. Had I grown bigger? My soul was an open cross taking in the beauty in a sponge-like attempt at total absorption. But where, really, did the beauty dwell? Out there in the leaden blue of the sea, in the blue-green of the mountains, or in the unknown horizon of myself? And I was suddenly afraid that my soul might flee from me, that its outstretched arms might never close, that it might remain forever crucified in the infinite ecstasy of its freedom. Freedom? A gust of wind sent its cold lash across my cheeks and I returned to the small insignificance of my flesh, and, once more the cable car was on its way down through tunnels of trees that did not smell of warmth. Alone with my small immensity, I could understand nothing. The roads of the world that might lead me to myself, to the warm, beautiful life that the evening wind of my fancy seemed to sing of, were long and varied. I bade an emotional farewell to the green light of the Brazilian foliage, and in the act of leave-taking, I again encountered, unexpectedly, the terrifying night of time, where the clear memories of youth fade and perish, where the gloomy prisons of ancient instinct emerge with death as their companion.

III

There, where the gloomy passions of ancient instinct emerge with death as their companion, every man is a deception for all other men. Fresh hopes lead to new disappointments as the mysterious, ambiguous signs of life and death pour the ultimate meanings of man into each existence. Truth and Falsehood.

That is why I feel both fragile and sublime as I traverse the tortuous paths of my buried heart. With infinite pity I alone can understand the lie that the others require of me. . .and truth? The monstruous and the horrible, can that be truth? Can truth be the nocturnal enchantment of the spirit of denial or the effort to be sincere concerning my intense denunciations and dark obsessions?

The most all-inclusive, the most enigmatic synthesis of my entire world occurs each time I return to my consciousness. And I am here again, in the temple of my loftiest imaginings. Who am I? I am the immense arch of the roadway, under which I must travel dragging my fear and my silence.

An ant slips across my leg. Prey to an inexorable, destructive force, I crush it with my finger. The sordid stain of a destroyed animal will remain on my skin and haunt me in my memory for a long time to come. I remember.

At home there used to be an ant hill in the patio, the earth perforated by a thousand holes. I felt then, as now, the same perverse desire to kill the ants and poured a pot of boiling water over that miniature ziggurat. Then I took a stick and destroyed their temple. I noted carefully the copper color of the dead bodies. The crazed survivors began removing the white eggs from their holes and commenced their flight in unrelenting mortal combat. But no, theirs was not a mortal combat, but a fight to live. Sustaining themselves in their fatigue by means of collective action, the ants brought out their dead and placed them on the slopes of the ruined mound. I began to feel like the carnivorous vulture of war. The pity created in me by their rapid, organized activity failed to conquer the vulture. I brought more water and threw it steaming onto the survivors. After a brief silence, the silence of the death that surrounds small things, I began the first phase of my stormy awakening from the ants' epoch. I was conscious of the merciless aspect of my realism. The light emerging from the shadows penetrated my awareness, from which the winged messengers were absent, and I was sad. Sadness was the symbol of my reality.

And here I am again in the temple of my loftiest imaginings. Laying my ear against the earth I hear the approach of footsteps. No, it is my heartbeat with its resounding echoes that ascend like ants along the sensitive legs of the bamboo cane. Yes, I hear steps. It is he approaching. Buddha, devil, poet, who is he? Each man is a deception for all other men. Beneath his steady, penetrating gaze, I feel the anguish of my disillusioned truth. The three women follow at a distance with their faces concealed as before. Their pace, as they glide along, is the slow pace of a nightmare or an enigma without answer. Obedient to the mad caprice of the Buddha, they draw near me, take my hands, lead me still deeper into the grove. I feel them unleash the force of my human rebellion and a sort of rancor and rebellion mixed fills me with hatred. The grove is like a strange room of white, naked walls with not a single piece of furniture to invite you to rest. Standing in its center, he devours the rigid frog. Its pupils stay suspended in space like two, odious mirrors which reflect my terror. I think that this is the setting for the tragic masquerade, the hypocrisies, all the absurdity of human existence. Where is my clothing? Where are my sandals and my mask? Are they going to question me? Where is my lie? I want to use it to cover myself. In what citadel of hallucinations am I imprisoned? Is this the great arena of corruption? Has this male being penetrated the depths of my tortuous heart? Will he murder or flagellate me? I am a captive in the narrow confines of his look. Suddenly, I feel my knees give way beneath the weight of my aged, tired heart.

Are my internal eyes the eyes of the frog? I have to close mine if I am to avoid seeing his, but my look is nailed to them by a strange force. I see my pale face and trembling lips as if tears were struggling to force their way out of a deep, deep lagoon. But I am not going to cry in front of people I do not know. In this realm of injustice a tear would have no value. I shall never let them know the bitter crystal of my soul. But why must I undergo the humiliation of their silence? Why don't they speak? Where is the beauty of the human voice? Where are the terrible questions for my terrible replies? Far more painful is the silent pain of experience now past. I know the anguish of vanquished truth. Who will anoint me with it so as to free me from it?

Man's reality is no more than the mortification of his imagination.

IV

Man's reality is no more than the mortification of his imagination. In the night of total disillusionment one leaves death behind and returns anew to life.

On Ipiranga Hill I waited for the sun to be born. The black clouds of darkness began to give birth to the light. The sea, shaking itself free of the night blanket that covered its nervous shoulders, began to beat its waves to foam. The sun, like a naked Venus, came forth from the mysterious womb and hurt my eyes with its light. The music of a silent epic deafened my ears. The great theater of the world and I were one. Within me, curtains, tinted with the rose and gold of the sky, were rising. The winged horses of the clouds were tracing the colors of their flight in allegories of emotion. I experienced a rebirth in that trembling, solitary dawn. Lost horizons returned to form their silhouettes in my endless inner worlds, where human magma stirs in restless poetry, where incandescence displays its flashing colors in the birth of life itself. And then, I heard Beethoven's music resounding in my ears. The sea was a shepherd with a flock of waves, the wind played its little flutes, and I witnessed with amazement my happiness. My happiness was you, a pronoun I had just invented. You, emerging from the bitter crystal of my soul. You, where I, the residue of a volcano, needed to be deposited. Life at that moment was love, and love the sweet sensation of living. Wherever you were, my hands were intertwined with yours. Our hands were five fingers doubled, joined but separated like the convention of the You/I pronouns. Unable to defeat the infinitesimal distance, which would forever hold them apart as they interlocked.

I, the opposite pronoun of You, thought of you. Thinking of you was the way I could make you most fully mine. How and for what purpose were you mine? So that I could invent myself anew, become myself again by being in your presence, because, just as night extinguishes day, day returns and comes full circle in the replenished power of the act of dawning. You knew me not. And so, I could surrender myself completely, repeat myself from beginning to end, reveal to you my depths, my valleys, my pools of calm, and in the mirror of your eyes contemplate the extravagance of my giving -- the stem of my soul growing heavenward -- hear the ancient charm of my new voice, feel on my bare shoulders the recovered caress of the non-silence within, there where musical vibrations do not lessen the rhythm of emotion as it speaks its silent language.

To love you was to love myself, to astonish you with me, to inspire your admiration with what I loved most; to love you was to give myself to you like the sweet white part of some exquisite bread, the miraculous manna of my creative imagination. To you, I was something precious which I found, while searching the untouched places of my Self. And **you,** you were the beauty that I invented. You, my reflection, which I saw in your eyes. You, the smile I placed on your lips. You, the trembling ecstacy of my passion. You were the mirror and I was Narcissus. Your love, the completed cycle of my reincarnation.

But you, my pronoun opposite, were a shallow, limited mirror. You did not have my boundless fantasy, and you made me recognize my tediousness. And then my words, and it was your fault, began to get repetitious. My voice began to tire, and your eyes showed me my everyday face. A separation began to appear between my solitude and yours, and the magic of the water that so charmed Narcissus was broken. That was how I sank again into the night of all disillusionments, there where death encounters its beginning.

V

There, where death encounters its beginning, you touched my shoulders; your hands of hemp dangled from my shoulders. My heels were dragged down by the gaze of your eyeless sockets. The whole night was a mantle woven from echoes and laments. And then I began to search the solitary grove.

"Let me enter through the door
Where Eve eats ants
And Adam fertilizes the dazzled fish.
Let me enter, you little horned man,
The grove of awakenings
And joyous leaps.

It was my voice of yore,
Which did not know the thick, bitter juices.
I feel it licking my feet
Beneath fragile, moist ferns.

Ay! Ancient voice of my love,
Voice of my truth,
Voice of my wounded side,
When all the roses flowed from my tongue
And the grass grew unafraid of the horses' ruthless teeth."

When all of the roses flowed from my tongue, your name turned bitter, for me, and the letters of your name fled from my skin like exiled ants. An inexorable, destructive force flowed through me and I crushed your memory with the clenched fist of forgetfulness. Now you were no more. Now you could never be. And still the sordid stain of a destroyed animal remained on my skin and haunted my memory for a long time.

Ay! Ancient voice of my love,
Voice of my truth,
Voice of my wounded side.

Where is the beauty of the human voice? Where are the terrible questions for my terrible replies? Why do that frog's open eyes stare at me so fixedly? Why do they question me in silence? Far more painful is the silent pain of experiences now past.

I shall not be able to complain
If I do not find what I once sought. . .

Kneeling on the earth, I felt the anguish of all the bamboo cane which witnessed my punishment. The Buddha's steady, penetrating gaze accused me silently. Of what?

> There beneath the roots and in the marrow of the air
> Lies understanding, the truth of error. . .

What were they accusing me of? What right had they to pry into my life? What deep secret did they want to steal from me? Ay! Voice of my wounded side, stop screaming!

> "No, I shall not scream!"
> "Yes! Scream, scream out your truth!"

Murderer, you murderer! Your teeth are salty with blood. Do you want my truth so that you can crush it to bits? Tell me who you are, you cruel judge of the wretched! Who are you? Why do you humiliate me with your silence? I hate you. I **hate** you. I hate **you**.

> There, neither the frost of lifeless eyes
> Nor the moans of the caterpillar-killed tree can enter.
> There, all forms, interlaced, maintain
> A single, frenzied expression of advance.

Nothing matters to me now. I have already said it. My tongue has hurled its venom. You pulled the word from my clenched teeth. I hate you for being nothing to me and for showing me my tediousness. I hate you because when I was alone with you I feared my solitude. I hate you for making me recognize my guilt so that now "I stumble haltingly through harsh, changeless eternity."

A thousand ants climb upon the Buddha's eyes. Am I supposed to crush them? Will I have to stain my fingernails again with the viscous copper of their bodies? No! I don't want to. Do not force me to do it.

The three women draw near me, take my hands, and pull me along with the slow, steady pace of nightmares and enigmas without answer. Suddenly, I am overwhelmed by a frenzied impulse to advance and without waiting further I plunge my fingers into the eyes of the Buddha.

I was in total darkness like a love without a dawn.

VI

I was in total darkness like a love without a dawn. What has become of you, the shattered illusion my eyes once beheld? What marble will give me the curved eloquence of what is now silent within me?

In Paris, the Louvre had been my forest of subtle discoveries. Paintings and statues were always waiting for me there, a changeless eternity of beauty, ready to reveal to me my most intimate feelings. Beside the visual images of those unvarying works of art, it was I who changed, growing inwardly and flowing like an endless river of emotion, feeling and desire. Although new to me the current of those feelings brought with them other sensations I had felt before.

The first time I beheld the **Victory of Samothrace**, only the external aspect drew my attention. I was astonished at the perfection captured in the marble. The folds of the tunic clinging to the body, the winged movement of the statue and each lighted part of the body brought me an instant revelation. In response to the artistic stimulus, intellect and memory harmonized their respective functions to make me feel through the dazzled eyes of a university student the appearance and existence of form, measured and verified by sight, in its contours -- height, width, and depth. What I'm saying is that those aspects the statue offered me, the quantitative ones, were external. But later, I managed to rid myself of some of the ideas drawn from the classroom and recognize, on my own, the artistic content in the form, the essence that made it live, the esthetic perception that brought on, almost unconsciously, a series of associations of ideas and feelings. So that my vision, attracted first by the surface, penetrated the special elements, the width and depth that made up the harmonious whole, and it was that essence specifically which made me take delight in my disinterested well-being. In other words, suddenly I was the field of action for the sculpture. Even though the marble mass was static in space, under its seductive power I was aware of widely ranging emotions and an intense spiritual passion.

The second time I went to Paris, I hastened excitedly to the re-encounter with my Victory, more a symbol for me now than a statue, a marble metaphor for what I knew. I felt enriched, like the winged figure, with centuries clinging to my shoulders while my arms reached out to life. I gazed at her in anxious contemplation, desiring to find your gaze. I wanted to discover you in your naked emotion before an object that stripped you bare. My eyes rested upon the crystalline surface of your eyes lingering there, fixed in time. I don't know if I loved you more or less in your absence/presence cast in marble. But in that more or that less, I loved myself because I loved you. And the Victory acquired another dimension which flowed through me.

Later. Both the future and the present are past. Experiences transformed to wings. Flights backward in time. Eternal nostalgia for the past. Something of me was left behind in that fixed eternity of beauty, and in our subsequent meetings disinterested well-being delights me no more.

What has become of you, the shattered illusion I once saw? In what marble figure am I to find again the eloquent contours of my bitter silence?

Time consumes and creates me. The forest of my hands holds a whisper of anguished caresses and every fiber of my skin responds to distant echoes of by-gone days destined for the eternity that is mine. My being is the point of departure for my meeting with the ultimate agony that I weave inside me, that confines me like an indivisible unity but makes me grow in response to the private demands of my private world. What has become of the importance, the deep meanings, of my thought? A moment in my history is developing through the life-giving word made of memories, through that alphabet that needs only to be used correctly for me to discover and understand even the most trivial symbolism of my spirit in its solitude. But, to what extent is it possible to explain with greater clarity what I am saying without falling into a false idealism or into a kind of intellectualism devoid of value? How difficult not to stumble over points of transition and reciprocity! My intimate need is my only guarantee for reaching a pure self-realization. But how can the subjective processes of the spirit be conveyed by clumsy, objective words?

The **Victory of Samothrace** uses the enchantment of her wings to retain the fleeting and the enduring. Her form is presumed to be her only means of expression, but I contend there is more, that in the material itself lies an infinite variety of line with dynamic qualities that create something internally visible and make it communicable, soft and lovely. From this contemplation of the senses there springs the symbol, in which I find again the crystalline surface of your eyes.

I see myself there, in each of the two pupils which have seen me, where something of me remains for the final reunion with myself. It must be, then, that paradise is an enormous pupil which encompasses us totally with one look. The grandeur of myself, my unique self, my indivisible self, will not fragment again into you and you, and I shall not feel anew that nostalgia for past disillusionments.

Body of white marble, here you will remain, stationary matter in external space, but when I return, you will have changed and in you I will find more solitude, resembling the dawn more nearly, and the shadows of love will be broader and more absorbing.

VII

The shadows of love will be broader and more absorbing.

"There all interlaced forms maintain
A single, frenzied expression as they advance. . ."

There is no sound of running fountains. There is no sound of water coming forth. The murmur of the wind goes unheard. I listen only to my solitude. I hear the darkness of silence and for the first time I contemplate the bitter surface of pain. The staring pupils of the frog bring me pain. It hurts to see myself in them, the way they see me. Or, am I like that? How can I recognize the deceiving lie? Is that my face? Are those my trembling lips? Is that smoldering ember my heart?

Like a single, frenzied expression of advance the three graces come forward. I see them again, nude and symbolically beautiful -- sexless, faceless bodies, which transfer to me the serenity of their silent enigma. Their hands are a world of revelations as they open the bamboo curtains and reveal horizons of enchantment. My knees no longer sink beneath their burden of pain into the earth of the grove but press upon the fine, dark sand of an open, solitary beach. Where the Buddha had been I see the sea. It is neither blue nor still but wild and dark like the sand violently agitated in its womb. The three mysterious graces lay me on my back on the beach, unfold my arms and spread apart my legs. And in that position of total freedom and abandon I experience the infinite pleasure of my heels buried in the sand while the immensity of the sky spreads above me like a splendid dome of diffused greys. The wind, a single, invisible seagull, beats its wings and I begin to feel the sticky sedative of the sea salt on my skin as it comes to me in roaring, whispering waves. The mystery is easily understood. I ask no questions. My tongue is silent and I do not think. My teeth do not chatter questions any longer nor do I have the nauseous feel of death in my fingers.

Like grey solitude they lie down beside me, motionless as an unborn song, present as the voice of conscience in the long corridors of silence. Who can they be? There is no sadness in the sky but neither is there any happiness. There is no anger in the sea but there is no sweetness there either. And in my heart there is neither passion nor indifference. In the surrounding stillness the profound dynamics of the expired truce begin to act. Again anguish flows up and through me -- a pale crab like the ones without shells that run in fright along deserted beaches. I want to shake myself with an abrupt leg movement, but I am still anchored to the sand with my arms forming a cross like some bloodless Christ, who can exclaim only, "My God, my God, why hast Thou forsaken me?"

I was still in my mother's womb when my unformed lips cried for the first time, "My God, my God, why hast Thou forsaken me?" You have imprisoned me in a world of solitude from whence you will cast me out wearing a flesh I do not desire." My cellular anguish listened for the first time to the palpitating ocean of the heart that nourished me in preparation for death. My first concave sky and empty beach were the uterus, where I floated, a yearning fetus, in the saline substance which destined me for transitory life, and where in the semi-darkness of my enclosure I encountered the mystery of unasked questions. It was there that the viscosity of death adhered beneath my nails, that unborn solitude clouded my soul with its melancholy breath and anguish provided soles for my feet. I was **born**, my fragile shoulders weighed down by the burden of this truth: Life is a regression toward death.

VIII

Life is a regression toward death. Grief and pain are its tribute, and solitude its most inhospitable place of exile. Theognis of Megora speaking through the lips of Silenus made this revelation to Midas:

> "It is better for Man never to have been born, never to have seen the piercing shafts of sunlight, and if he is already born, then it is best for him to hasten to the grave and find repose beneath the thick covering of earth."

Gnomic poetry? Song of profound pessimism? Truth can have no other form. I seek and when I find it, its face is always hidden in its hands.

But, why solitude? I have five fingers on each hand and, in spite of all, I alone possess my being in the confines of my own heart.

I remember. It was in Pindal's cave in Asturias that I saw the painting by prehistoric man. He had painted an elephant with its heart in the center on the rock. Although scholars attribute magical intent to these pictures of animals, they are really only paintings of a state of mind. All humanity is little more than one man, a prehistoric man in the shelter of a cave, while air, rain and time weave his immense tunic of solitude. And the poor cave man depicted solitude in the immensity of an elephant with himself just a little, palpitating heart at its center!

That is why I raise my voice to call you and display my solitude in my anxious desire for your compassion. But do you understand the language of words and can you feel pity toward a neighbor? No, do not think I call out to you. It is for me that my voice clamors. For the first time, I discover myself as a pre-Adam entity, a protozoan cell from earlier millenia, when life had its origin in Cambrian solitude and predestined me for my present self. To find myself I must go back to my paleozoic North where silence consisted of membranes and I was an indivisible nucleus where my present had its beginning, where my end resides. Meanwhile along the way I find my own fossil fields. Here is a truth billions of years old: only in solitude can I have my being.

But why do I tremble? And why do the eyes of that frog reflect my terror? Why does a scream knot my throat? Why do I call for mercy? How many times have I hated my heart and repudiated the tenderness I was offered? How many times have I killed in my thoughts?

Whims, caprices, billions of them, have taken me away from my solitude. Oh yes, rancor is one of the fundamental whims. Bitter and thick on the tongue, heavy and burning in the heart, it is a crippling sore on the soles of the feet. When there is rancor, one is not alone but accompanied by another who makes us acutely uneasy. That is when our hands dip into evil blood and life imposes on us the stench of viscous, acid death.

Rancor is what I learned from you. I never loved you so much as when I hated you. But take care, do not distort my meaning. Loving is not now so beautiful as the desire to love. Love implies an eternal presence, domination, utter destruction. I hated you in all my thoughts, binding you with them till you could no longer be alone with your solitude nor I with mine.

Later, there was tedium. My anger was spent. Suddenly, I realized that I hated you no more; I drew away from you forever and my house, wider and more spacious now, again harbored my solitude alone.

Today, as you see, I can speak of you as one speaks of the weather and I can enter the heart of the grove without longing for you.

You will never know which "you" was you. I have sentenced you to be a second-person pronoun and you are becoming merged with that alien generality, which I leave behind so that I may find my own salvation.

What is my salvation? From what sentence am I being freed? Why was I condemned? For having been born? Those eternal, unanswerable questions that have the ring of empty philosophy!

The why and the where do not matter. All that concerns me is the present that is mine at this moment and this miraculous, tormenting grove where I find myself.

Fear. The bamboo canes shake their feathered headdresses in the air and I lose track of time. To lose the sense of time is to become its master. And the time that lies in my hands frightens me. Its totality gives me a greater possession of myself. Never before have I known such inner riches as now that I am alone, a vast continent of soul and thought in which to discover myself. I am what I have lived and more. I am all that remains to me to live. Toward it, I journey, toward my finality, that which in common speech we call destiny and which is nothing other than the re-encounter of the beginning.

Now they approach. Now I hear them. I recognize their footsteps in the darkness. They come to take me to those despairing, supreme confessions, to that pleasant terror which signals the return of life. No, they are not phantoms. Phantoms lack composition and the reasoned beauty of form. But they advance in an aura of fantastic human qualities. In their half-hidden faces I perceive for the first time the shadowed splendor of tears. Do they impel me toward pity or pain?

Somber, motionless time becomes an impromptu stage and I find that I am in a plaza beneath an immense, mournful sky and in the center, completing the fundamental theme, is a coffin made of bamboo. With gentle tyranny they push me toward it. The three women raise the lid so that I see the intensely pale face of the Buddha, who lies within, his arms resting across his chest. A tragic shadow rests upon his greenish-yellow lips. In his pallor I seem to find the ancient meaning of death; yet, just when I am on the verge of succumbing to nostalgia at his loss, they open his thorax with a surgical knife and reveal to my astonished eyes his beating heart, rapacious and implacable in its absolute monopoly of life. That was when my cry traversed the air like a dagger.

IX

That was when my cry traversed the air like a dagger and the bamboo echoed it with a huge sonorous grimace.

A scream. For how many centuries had I been silent! My throat hurt from the vibrations. A deep crevice opened in the living rock and the ants spilled out in disorder and fright. My clumsy, splendid scream was beginning to acquire the character of a mysterious spectacle of life. Yes, a spectacle in its most profound sense because it reflected all the vital drama of chance and all the dark forces governing the anxiety and anguish of life. The army of ants, shaken by my cry, fled like an army of shades and specters, thirsty shadows which live in the dark hollow of the human heart.

My scream exploded in signs and images and the combination of its echoes, reverberating from cane to cane, traced the only possible itinerary for my exit from the grove.

My voice in its infinite richness burst the supreme limits of the imaginary and once more I found myself confronting absurd, merciless reality, experiencing the senseless delight of ordinary existence, feeling the moist earth beneath my toes and seeing the perpendicular, opaque grove with its yellow green cane. Once more, I was faced with the halting escape from myself.

Outside the grove the burning sun and twenty thousand white flamingos would be waiting.

Where, oh where, is the arrow which points the way? I must quicken my step. I must emerge from this vast, heavy dream that holds me.

No, no it is no dream. It is the beginning of the heat.
Now, I smell the slime of the swamp.
Now, I anticipate the green treachery of the crocodiles.
Now, I see close by the garden of azaleas.

There, distant, far behind me the pagoda remains. The Buddha is young, beardless, smiling, a poet dreaming among bamboo whispers.

TRIPTYCH

Translated by Arney L. Strickland

I

I was dreaming, yes dreaming. . .and in that dream I was about to wake up. When I opened my eyes, I saw that I was dead. A woman was putting a shroud on me, and upon touching me, she was amazed at not finding me rigid. I myself was aware of the resiliency of my limbs and to show it I stretched a little. Then the woman put boots and spurs on me, absurdly inappropriate for such an occasion. But soon I understood that all of this was for a reason. At the foot of my bed, stage curtains opened which revealed an interesting scene. I saw a road going up a hill, at the bottom of which an old silver-gray and barebacked horse was waiting to transport me to another world. Some invisible beings helped me to mount, and slowly I began the journey. At times, and always uphill, I pushed the ground with my feet to help the animal climb. I don't know why, but we soon stopped at a plaza, or park, with iron railings covered with bougainvilleas. The pavement was mosaic and lined with street lamps. I recalled with nostalgia the Plaza of Portugal.

The second stop was a very special place, encircled by shrubs covered with **lágrimas de San Pedro.**[1] I gathered some and examined them in the palm of my hand, then I felt burdened with a gray nostalgia. But I remembered that I was dreaming.

The third stop brought me to a round platform floating in an immense sea of silence. Then I was myself standing in its center. The horse had disappeared. It was then I knew that I had arrived at my own solitude.

When I awoke from both dreams, my eyes truly were closed and I was dead.

II

I didn't know the place at all, nor did I know how I got there. I approached a man who looked like a guard and asked him to show me how to get to the address which I had on a card. Without a word he showed me the street where we were and then gestured that I should turn right at the next corner. This I did and ran into a strange street scene. A crowd had gathered to watch, and with the natural curiosity of a passerby, I joined them to see what was going on. In the center of the mob, two women were struggling, mother and daughter, and like a late arriver at a play, I couldn't tell whether the mother was beating the daughter or whether, on the contrary, she was helping her in some way. Suddenly the scene changed and I saw myself and these people accompanying a funeral car. We arrived at the cemetery and I found myself in front of the people facing a square open grave site. At its edge lay a woman's body dressed in a sheer white nightgown. The dead woman's mother, at the head of the bier, was caressing the daughter and dropping petals on her, for they were about to

-----
[1]St. Peter's Tears; hard, gray tear-shaped berries.

inter the coffin. It was then that I heard a deafening murmur of shock and fear as the corpse suddenly sat up and before our eyes arose in flight through the air.

It was a light, ethereal sensation, neither giddy nor anxious that I felt on wings of air. But striving to rise higher, I again observed the burial scene.

The terror of the group was changed to a voiceless murmur of impatience. The mother still was dropping a nostalgic shower of petals upon the corpse, thus avoiding the gloom of her actual interment, but the others were eager to close the grave before the dead one might escape.

I was in the front row. I removed a green muslin handkerchief which was around my neck and let it fall, like one more petal, upon the corpse. Suddenly a cloud of dust arose; and again, as though scoffing, the dead woman rose in flight.

> To rise like a vertical sigh,
> crossing the radiant day,
> angelical and light
> like love that moves the universe.

All the spectators frantically reached up to seize the corpse by the feet to prevent a second escape. The dead woman felt the weight of their bodies hanging from her frail heels and tried harder and freed herself. She went up and up vertically and, then, stretching herself out like a leaf on the face of the wind, she flew over towers and castle gardens whose flagstones showed scars of the past, of crosses and of tears.

Again I saw the burial scene. The impatient crowd tried to force me to throw the first spade of dirt upon the coffin. I felt stiff like my legs were paralyzed, and refused to do it, just because I was in the front row; I crossed my arms tightly over my chest and closed my eyes. A deafening murmur arose and then I knew that the dead one had risen on her third and final flight.

III

I found myself inside a huge eye, mahogany colored, and through its transparent cornea, the world round about was wrapped in shades of cognac. Life was a mansion of large rooms and there, in its center, blazed a wild bonfire under a magnificent framework of carved copper. On the fire, I saw a gigantic frying pan of boiling oil. I realized then that this was the altar where I would witness the ceremony destined for me. And I was not mistaken. The succeeding ritual scenes which I saw occurred simultaneously with the blinks of that Cyclopean eye that encompassed me.

He approached. His head was shaven and his gestures and dress were like a Buddhist monk. He walked slowly; his bare feet over monastic sandals seemed pious and beautiful, and I felt overcome with a sudden ecstatic emotion. Nevertheless, the following scene removed me from that preternatural state of the soul, for I saw him executing an absurd culinary rite that, to me, became grotesque and condemnable, despite his beatific and priestly appearance. Actually I saw him beating eggs and pouring them into the huge frying pan. When the foamy mixture of whites and yolks doubled, he took the frying pan by the handle and expertly threw the tortilla into the air to turn it. The eye blinked then, and in that mohogany obscurity in which I saw myself submerged for an instant, I thought how strange and incomprehensible was the theater of life.

The tortilla, symbol of a gigantic Host, was hanging like a gong in the center of the dining room. All of them were gathering around. Who? They were Tahitian women, like those that Gauguin painted, but the most extraordinary thing is that, naked to the waist, they exhibited a strip of dark and wrinkled skin which extended from the shoulders to the nipples, that, at first sight, was deceiving, since their nakedness seemed more like a blouse with straps. Performing an impressive dance, they prepared a gourd cup of chocolate. The color of cocoa was reflected like a blaze in the mahogany brilliance of their pupils. They approached with that foamy nectar to the place where the monk was. He raised the cup toward the Cyclopean altar of the mystery that enwrapped me and, in that instant, behind the crystal cornea of silence, I saw his eyes. They had the expression of a vulturous bird of prey. And, then I discovered that he was drinking a toast with the very blood of my death.

The Quest for Self-knowledge and Reconciliation in "La Isla de Avery"

Kathleen M. Glenn

Twentieth-century literature abounds in pessimistic portrayals of alienation and spiritual negativism. The Costa Rican writer Victoria Urbano, however, articulates a vision of life which while recognizing the reality of negative forces transcends despair and rises from anguish to affirmation. In order to elucidate that vision the present study will focus upon a structural and thematic analysis of "La Isla de Avery." This story is included in the collection **Y era otra vez hoy** which was awarded the Premio Internacional de Literatura "León Felipe" in 1969.[1]

Urbano has expressed her admiration for Unamuno, stating that he is one of the writers who has influenced her most.[2] Like Unamuno for whom fiction is synonymous with philosophy,[3] Urbano uses her story to explore the meaning of existence, and her protagonist is an **agonista** who moves in a fictional world characterized by its **desnudez**. It is inner, subjective reality rather than the external objective world which is her main concern. Although the immediate stimulus for the story was a visit to Avery Island, the physical locale is less important than the symbolism of the island (a metaphor for isolation) and certain of its features. The narrative voice is that of a nameless figure, and the choice of the "I as Protagonist" point of view facilitates reader identification with the narrator as a generalized representative of humanity. She is the universal "I" attempting to find order and meaning in a seemingly chaotic and incoherent world. Clock time is unimportant to the introspective, retrospective vision of the protagonist as she turns inward and explores her psyche. The development of the story is non-linear as memories of former experiences, allusions to art and literature, reflections upon past and present, dreams, and hallucinations are all interwoven.

The structure of the story combines a circular movement with a ternary grouping.[4] The choice of these particular patterns is significant because of the religious symbolism of the circle and of the number three. The circle is a traditional symbol of heaven, perfection, unity, and wholeness, and the number three symbolizes spiritual synthesis, is associated with the concepts of heaven and Trinity, and represents the solution to the conflict posed by dualism.[5] Both symbols are frequent in Urbano's work. Her poem **Los nueve círculos** describes the nine concentric circles of heaven and earth which are "la trinidad multiplicada,"[6] and the number three is the informing principle of the story "Tríptico."[7] The triptych is, of course, divided into three sections. In the first the traveler stops at three stations. In the second the corpse which is about to be buried rises and flies through the air three times; there are three references to the murmurs of the spectators at the burial; and the dead woman who is witnessing her own interment three times finds herself "en primera fila" among the mourners. The third section consists of three paragraphs which describe a series of ritual scenes. Each division of the story ends with a moment of mental perception or discovery: "Supe entonces que," "entonces comprendí que," and "entonces, supe que." In "La Isla de Avery" the ternary structure is more complex, as will be shown.

Briefly, the story can be seen as the account of a figurative journey, a quest for self-knowledge, and a coming to terms with the reality of the human condition. The narrator-protagonist sets out in search of the forest of giant bamboo trees. The forest is an image of the inner self, the "bosque interno/por donde se camina solemnemente,/ y donde todo pormenor se observa/en provecho del más íntimo/espacio de la calavera" (NC, p. 37). In literature the forest is frequently a symbol of the unconscious and is depicted as a place of evil which harbors dangers and demons.[8] The story is divided into nine sections. In the first six the dualism of life and the conflict between good and evil is revealed in the alternation of positive and negative features. The tension between the two is resolved in the final three sections where solitude and death are accepted. The ternary pattern is enclosed within the circular movement of the protagonist's journey. The story ends with the same description of the Buddha -- "El buda es joven, imberbe, sonriente. Es el poeta que sueña entre los susurros del bambú" (p. 147) -- which appeared near the beginning. The final phrase of each section is repeated at the beginning of the following one. This pattern continues throughout the nine sections and serves to bind one to another. The first section with its encompassing vision of both spirit and matter is subdivided into two parts. The phrase "he quedado como suspiro de árbol en tierra" appears near the end of the first part, is repeated word for word at the beginning of the second negative part, and reappears in the modification "vuelvo a sentirme como suspiro de arbol en tierra" which is the concluding phrase of section I and the initial one of section II. (This "vuelvo" stresses the idea of circular movement.)

A fairly detailed examination of the first and lengthiest section will reveal the symbolic nature of the story, its principal motifs, and the positive-negative pattern of sections I to VI. The protagonist sets out in the dusty heat of the afternoon in search of the cool, green, shady bamboo forest. The opposition between animality and spirituality is immediately brought out in the description of the treacherous crocodiles lurking in the muddy waters of the swamp and the purity of the flamingos which are a lake of snow, an island of plumage and beauty. (The protagonist later speaks of her soul as "una isla de pluma y belleza" [p. 123].) En route she passes the pagoda of a young, smiling Buddha, the poet who dreams in a world of bamboo and crystal. The figure of the Buddha is employed by Urbano to represent "al poeta que todos llevamos dentro, o a Dios-poeta, o a la imaginación que a veces puede hacer de Buda su propio terror."[9] Descriptions of the physical setting -- the marshes, bird sanctuary, and jungle gardens of Avery Island in southern Louisiana -- are

103

interlaced with memories and references to works of art. The echoing solitude brings to mind Edgar Allan Poe's "Annabel Lee." Contrasts of light and shadow in the forest remind her of the film **Rashomon,** and the vertical stalks of the bamboo summon up Velazquez' painting the **Surrender of Breda**. The olive color of the stalks makes her think of the dark-skinned Egyptian god Osiris and Ramses II.[10]

A parallel is drawn between man and the tall straight bamboo trees which are rooted to the ground and yet tower above it. The character finds herself momentarily immobilized by the slender cords which bind her feet to the earth, but although earthbound she is crowned with "una melena suelta de suenos, de recuerdos, de presentimientos, de ideas, de soledades" (p. 123). The recollection of having experienced years before a similar sensation of returning to the earth leads her to reflect upon the cyclical nature of existence: "Es que pasamos una y otra vez por nosotros mismos, recorriéndonos en ciclos, reencontrándonos en el mismo lugar donde primero nos hallamos" (p. 123). As the light fades the shadows become filled with the creations of her imagination and a reciprocal transformation takes place. The bamboos become personified while she finds herself turning into a tree, "suspiro de árbol en tierra" (p. 124). The change makes her recall Bernini's sculpture of Daphne's metamorphosis into a laurel.

At this point in the narrative there is a dramatic change and "las imágenes de la vida pasan a imágenes de muerte en un abierto y paradójico drama de existencia. . .La noche desciende desesperada sobre la meseta del trágico destino humano" (pp. 126, 127). The protagonist is plunged into a nightmarish witches' Sabbath filled with Goyesque figures, and the previous vision of a world of beauty filled with creations of the intellect and of the spirit vanishes. It is replaced by a shadowy world of madness and violence in which cruelty and evil appear to be rampant. The beginning of the descent into darkness is marked by the climbing of an ant over her body. Because of their multiplicity, the connotation of ants is generally unfavorable, and J. E. Cirlot calls attention to an Indian myth in which ants symbolize the pettiness and fragile character of existence.[11] Three mysterious female figures approach and lead her deeper into the forest where she witnesses their sacrificing of a frog. The women first destroy its brain and then cut open its chest and do a cardiogram. As she watches the action of the heart being recorded she wonders in terror if that is all life is, a diagram of peaks and waves registered upon a graph. The dilated pupils of the frog are a mirror in which she sees the ambiguity and absurdity of her own being. As if hypnotized she dips her fingers into the frog's blood, and the sight of her bloodstained nails reminds her of Goya's **Duel with Cudgels** with its two men sunk in the mud desperately battling one another. The Buddha, no longer a dreaming, golden-voiced poet, is transformed into a devil disguised as a goat symbolizing the power of the negative, dark forces which are a part of human existence. Clothed in a surgeon's gown he snips the tenuous thread of life of the frog, and then he undergoes one further metamorphosis and Saturn-like devours the frog as time devours its creatures. Horrified, the protagonist falls fainting to the ground. As section I ends she regains consciousness and once again feels herself "suspiro de árbol en tierra" (p. 127).

The alternation of the positive and the negative, light and darkness, spirituality and animality continues in sections II through VI. Section I has provided an overview of human existence and has established the pattern which will prevail in the next five sections. The positive vision with which the first section began is continued in sections II, IV, and VI. In sections III and V there is a return to the negative vision, marked by the reappearance of ants, the Buddha, and the three women.

As section II begins black night and its wall of silence have been displaced by a luminous world of colors, "colores resonantes. . .amarillos. . .un azul claro. . .colores puros" (p. 128) and "un abierto canto de juventud" (p. 128). The protagonist finds herself on the shores of a fantastic lake of memories, memories of the gardens of the Palace of Aranjuez, of a Good Friday procession in Avila, and of the stone figure of Christ atop Corcovado in Río de Janeiro. The earlier parallel between the bamboo trees and men, both of which rise above the earth in which they are rooted, is further developed in the description of the vines which climb up the trees "con ansias de cielo, pero se enmaranan sin alcanzar nunca lo que buscan" (pp. 129-30). In a similar fashion man strives to reach upward but all too often becomes entangled in a labyrinthine world and fails to attain what he seeks. Although dwarfed by the Christ figure, while the protagonist stands beside it on the mountaintop her soul seems to expand and embrace a world of beauty, but as she descends from Corcovado night reappears. The symbolism of this ascending-descending movement is found throughout the story. Human existence swings between the two poles of hope and disillusionment, truth and falsehood, life and death.

In section III as the protagonist traverses the tortuous paths of her inner self the destructive forces latent within her are exteriorized in her crushing of an ant which is crawling along one of her legs. The same perverse desire she now feels had led her on an earlier occasion to pour a kettle of boiling water over an anthill. Like a vulture she had hovered over the scene of destruction and had then dumped a second kettle over the survivors. The three women reappear and lead her deeper into the forest which has turned into a strange room in the center of which the Buddha is devouring the frog. This is the room of the tragic masquerades, hypocrisies, and absurdity of human existence. The bareness of the room corresponds to the character's own nakedness as she stands stripped of clothing or falsehoods with which to cover herself. The capacity for cruelty and hatred which lie within her "corazon subterraneo" (p. 131) have been unmasked.

This somber vision of men (women) as vulturine creatures which are the prisoners of their own animal passions gives way in section IV to the recollection of a sunrise seen from the Morro of Ypiranga. As light, color, and music flooded the world the character also was "reborn" through the experience of love which appeared to promise further self-discovery and completion. She became "el gran teatro del mundo," knowing no limits and embracing all infinity within her being. The tú to which she gave herself was the incarnation of her joy, the mirror in which Narcissus-like she saw herself reflected. But the mirror turned out to lack depth, to be a "hueco de capacidad limitada" (p. 135), and she fell back into her own radical solitude.

In section V the destructive forces which earlier had led her to crush an ant now compel her to smash with the clenched fist of forgetfulness the memory of the tú she had once loved. The accusing eyes of the Buddha wrest from her the secret of her hatred for the tú who failed to live up to her expectations and who made her recognize her guilt as a descendant of Eve: "Te odio porque fuiste nada para mí. Te odio porque me hiciste conocer el tedio de mí misma. Te odio porque a solas contigo temí mi soledad. Te odio porque me hiciste conocer mi culpa y ahora 'tropiezo vacilante por la dura eternidad fija'" (p. 137). The character's recognition and voicing of her hatred act as a cleansing. Once more the three women approach her, but this time the phrase which was used on the two previous occasions -- "me internan aún más por el bosque" -- is not repeated, for the character has reached the center of the forest. In one last impulse of violence she plunges her fingers into the ant-filled eyes of the Buddha.

In section VI, the concluding one of this first block, the narrator recalls the Louvre which was for her a place of spiritual communion. The paintings and sculptures revealed to her her own self, and each successive visit led to new illumination. When she saw the **Winged Victory of Samothrace** she was first entranced by its formal perfection. Later her appreciation deepened as she penetrated beneath the external form to the inner essence which animated the statue. And the statue became a metaphor of her own existence, enriched by the weight of the past behind her and leaning forward with arms extended into the future. She, like the statue, is caught poised between past and future, and each passing moment of time destroys and yet creates her. The past can be recaptured through memories which are "vuelos hacia atrás" (p. 139). As the character strives to understand herself and her world she asks "¿cómo podré ilustrar los procesos subjetivos de mi espíritu con la tosca objetividad de la palabra?" (p. 140). The question reflects the frustration of the artist who struggles to express abstractions and nuances of feeling through the medium of a language which lacks the necessary precision and subtlety. The phrase "intelecto y memoria compaginaron sus respectivas operaciones" (p. 138) suggests the method which must be followed if one is to fathom the enigmas of existence, and it also describes the manner in which Urbano has composed the story, calling upon intellect and memory, intertwining past and present.

The protagonist is now ready for "el reencuentro final conmigo misma" (p. 140). The three remaining sections of the story will focus upon solitude and death. In a recent interview, Victoria Urbano commented upon the significance in her work of these two themes:

La soledad es mi palacio de trabajo, "mi castillo interior" donde vislumbro todo el panorama de la vida y donde medito sobre su fin inevitable que es la muerte. Aunque una sea parte de la otra, sólo sé que para "vivir la muerte" hay que "morir la vida" y este misterio absoluto me asombra, me inquieta y me hace apegarme más a la vida que tengo. De este modo la muerte se me torna intelectualmente conflictiva y poética. Mejor dicho, yo hago poesía filosófica alrededor de la muerte pues es la única forma en que puedo acercarme a ella sin temor.[12]

Both solitude and death are important motifs in **Los nueve círculos**, which bears an intimate relationship to "La Isla de Avery." The epigraph for the poem is "En la soledad se encuentra la profundidad verdadera." Man's solitude is seen as punishment for the sin of Adam and Eve. Prior to the Fall, ". . .el hombre fue su propio paraiso / y Eva fue su propia ilusion / y su carne fue su propia pureza / y su soledad fue su propia compania" (NC, p. 9). The Garden of Eden was "aquel huerto sellado / donde no entraba doña Soledad" (NC, p. 24), and the first **tú** and **yo**, Adam and Eve, were one flesh. But since the Fall and the expulsion from Paradise man has been condemned to wander the earth in solitude, to know that he is a finite being. On reaching the eighth circle, "La soledad," there is a serene acceptance of solitude:

Ya no se busca el rostro
en el narciso espejo,
ni el cuerpo siente su tensión dramática,
ni la trágica inquietud
marca huellas en los labios. (NC. p. 37)

Anguish is left behind and in the closing lines of the circle there is a new feeling of plenitude:

he salido ya del túnel de la noche
para hallarme plena
en mi plena soledad
de puerta hacia la muerte. (NC, p. 39)

The correspondence between certain lines of the eighth circle and phrases used in "La Isla de Avery" is clear:

En el bosque de mis manos
hay un susurro de caricias
que retumban ecos en la eterna
soledad silente de mí misma.
                    (NC, p. 39)

No se oyen fuentes correr.
No se oye agua nacida.
No se oye susurrar al viento.

Sólo escucho mi soledad
en lo blando oscuro del silencio.
                    (NC, p. 39)

En el bosque de mis manos hay un susurro
de caricias angustiadas, y toda mi piel
retumba ecos de ayeres acunados para la
eternidad de mí misma.
                    (pp. 139-40)

No se oyen fuentes correr. No se oye
agua nacida. No se oye el susurro del viento.
Sólo escucho mi soledad.
Oigo lo oscuro del silencio.
                    (p. 141)

In the ninth circle, "La muerte," the lost paradise will be regained:

allí, en la verde ausencia del dolor y la miseria,
libre por siempre de la honda pena de la muerte,
limpia y olvidada del abismo del pecado,
mis brazos sin cadenas de tiempo,
mis rodillas sin la humillación de lo mortal,
mis pies sin el terror del caminante humano,
  mi corazón, regocijo palpitante de esperanza!
                    (NC, p. 42)

A similar movement of liberation and ascension is found in the last three sections of "La Isla de Avery."

In section VII the three feminine figures approach, but they are now the three Graces of mythology. They lead the protagonist to a solitary beach and stretch her out on the sand beneath the dome of the heavens. Bathed by the soothing waters of the sea, she is enveloped by a feeling of tranquillity and release. But the respite is only temporary, and with the return of anguish she cries out "My Lord, my Lord, why hast Thou forsaken me?" (P. 142). The experience on the beach is a figurative return to the womb which was her first confinement, her first "cielo cóncavo, playa hueca donde yo, feto anhelante, flotaba en el salino sabor que me destinaba al tránsito de la vida" (p. 142). From that womb of solitude she was expelled into the world, burdened with the knowledge that "la vida es un desandar hacia la muerte" (p. 142).

In the Cave of Pindal in Asturias she found her own solitude expressed in the cavemen's painting of an elephant. The tiny heart beating in the center was man, dwarfed by the immensity of his loneliness. Her recollection in section VIII of the prehistoric painting is an important step toward the moment of enlightenment in which she realizes that solitude is the very essence of man: "Yo solo puedo ser en soledad" (p. 144). Only by recognizing and accepting the inevitablility of that solitude can one attain to the "self-possession" and fulfillment implicit in the protagonist's "nunca me he visto tan rica de mí misma como ahora que me tengo a solas, vasto continente de alma y pensamiento para descubrirme. Soy todo lo que he vivido, pero aún más, soy todo lo que me falta por vivir. Y a eso voy, a mi finalidad, a lo que en lengua vulgar llamamos destino y que es tan sólo el reencuentro del comienzo" (p. 145). In section I she experienced the sensation of having lived in other centuries and having known other existences. That feeling is now developed into the recognition of her oneness -- in solitude -- with all humanity. Before emerging from the forest there is one last brief moment of fear when she sees the three women lift the lid of the bamboo coffin in which the Buddha lies and cut open his chest, baring the beating heart.

The beginnning of section IX is punctuated by the protagonist's scream which sunders the bare rocks and sends the ants fleeing like an army of shades and specters. The scream shatters the imaginary world in which she has been immersed and marks the return to reality. "Otra vez experimenté la estúpida alegría de la existencia cotidiana" (p. 147). Once again she finds herself back at the edge of the forest beyond which lie a bright sun, the whiteness of the flamingos, and the crocodiles of the swamp. And behind her lies the pagoda with its dreaming Buddha. The protagonist has returned to the point from which her quest began, to a world of spirituality and animality. But the journey into the forest has functioned as a catharsis. She has become reconciled to the dualism of her nature and is enriched by the knowledge she has gained. She can now speak of the joy of daily existence even though it be a "stupid"joy. In a dialectical process, the contradiction of opposites (thesis and antithesis) of sections I to VI has been resolved in the synthesis of sections VII to IX. The protagonist has faced up to the tension between positive and negative forces and has accepted the fact that being is synonymous with solitude and that life is "un desandar hacia la muerte." Death will be a liberation of the spirit from the flesh in which it is imprisoned and a completion of the circle of perfection.

Notes

[1]"La Isla de Avery," pp. 119–47.

The story was originally titled "Y era otra vez hoy." References will be included in the text.

[2]Interview with Victoria Urbano, February 12, 1976. **Letras Femeninas**, Vol. 2, No. 1, Spring 1976, pp. 5–12.

[3]See Chapter IV, "La novela como método de conocimiento," of Julián Marías, **Miguel de Unamuno**, 3rd ed. (Madrid: Espasa-Calpe, 1960).

[4]For a fascinating analysis of numerological and symmetrical patterns in literature see R. G. Peterson, "Critical Calculations: Measure and Symmetry in Literature," PMLA, 91 (1976), 367–75.

[5]J. E. Cirlot, **A Dictionary of Symbols**, trans. Jack Sage (New York: Philosophical Library, 1962), pp. 45, 222.

[6]**Los nueve círculos** (Madrid: Ediciones Castilla de Oro, 1970), p. 11, hereafter cited in the text as NC.

[7]"Tríptico," pp. 93–95.

[8]Cirlot, p. 107. A notable example of this forest symbolism is found in Nathaniel Hawthorne's "Young Goodman Brown."

[9]Interview with Victoria Urbano.

[10]Both figures have a religious connotation. Ramses II is believed to be the pharaoh of Exodus, and Osiris was linked with the doctrine of immortality.

[11]Cirlot, pp. 13–14.

[12]Interview. The phrase "castillo interior" and the paradoxical "vivir la muerte" and "morir la vida" call to mind the figure of Santa Teresa. In **Las moradas**, a treatise upon the soul and its relationship with God, Santa Teresa allegorically describes the soul as a castle of seven chambers or mansions. In the innermost chamber the soul is united with God. According to Santa Teresa self-knowledge is the path to knowledge of God.

5

RIMA VALLBONA

RIMA VALLBONA

Born in San José, Costa Rica in 1931, she obtained her Master's Degree in Liberal Arts from the University of Costa Rica; later took some courses at Salamanca, Spain and Paris, France and is now working on her doctoral dissertation.

Married to a Catalonian, Dr. Carlos Vallbona, they have two sons and three daughters.

For many years Rima was Chairman of Spanish at St. Thomas University, Houston, where she now devotes her time fully to teaching.

But above all, Rima is a dedicated writer. In 1968 she shared with Alfonso Chase the Costa Rican Prize "Aquileo J. Echeverría" for her novel **Noche en Vela** (Editorial Costa Rica). Last August 26, 1977 she became one of the three Costa Rican winners of the contest for short stories "Jorge Luis Borges", sponsored by Fundación Givré in Buenos Aires, Argentina.

She has two more books forthcoming. One of them, **Mirror of Loneliness** (Vantage Press) includes some short stories in collaboration with her daughter, Nuri.

Her other published books are:

Polvo del camino (Lehmann, San José, C.R. 1971, short stories)

Yolanda Oreamuno (Ministerio de Cultura, C.R. 1972, study)

CHUMICO TREE
Fable

Pressed against the shabby school house, the chumico tree bears a miraculous fruit for the poor child who cannot afford marbles.

When the poor child runs, the chumicos, black wealth of infinite roundness, fill his pockets with a muffled jingle, a chant of dreams that will follow his school hours of numbers, adjectives, north-bound rivers, volcanoes: Poas, Barba, Irazu, Turrialba. . .

Ah, the delight of escape: now without hunger and poverty, past barefeet, ragged shirt and patches, the boy opens the ritual by drawing the magic circle in the dust. Each hour turns into a whiff of time, a triumphant cry, a wild enjoyment. Tic. . . Tic. . . Tic. . . The chumicos boldly knock against each other in the enchanting circle of dust.

The recess bell rings and the children run to the chumico tree to see if it is finally time to pick its fruit. "Here, Paco, one for me." "No, you have too many." "Throw me those three, Chalo." "Pepe, don't be mean to me, Look, I don't have any." "One. Just one for me." Anita begs humbly, trying to make herself heard over the screams and uproars of the harvest.

"You want one?" Chalo looks scornfully at the patchless uniform, the patent-leather shoes, and the small white, clean hands of Anita. Everyone looks at her like Chalo does, through the pride of their barefeet and their mended uniforms. Atop the chumico tree, Chalo spits down at her, but she manages to dodge the spit.

"That's for you, meat-head! Have your rich daddy buy the chumicos with his money. If you come near here, you'll see what we'll give you."

On the way home, Anita wonders whether or not it is time for the first shoot of her penny tree to sprout. "Plant a few pennies and you'll have it!" said Eufrasia, the maid — Chalo's mother — who filled her imagination with stories of elves and ghosts. Anita planted her coins under the peach tree and waited impatiently with grand illusions. She wished that clocks and calendars would devour time until she would finally find herself in the highest limb of her penny tree, full of golden coins shining in the sun, ready for harvest: For you, Paco, for you, four pennies. And you, María, have seven so that you won't push me or trip me. Here comes nine pennies for you, Ophelia, but let me play ball. If you don't cuss at me, Pepe, I'll give you ten. Chalo, Chalito, be good like your mother, will you give me a chumico? Just one teeny-tiny ripe chumico and I'll give you all the pennies you want.

Where Anita planted the coins there is only a circle marked by stakes and the moistness of the ground, watered many-times-over with hopes that one day her nasty school friends would say that she is equal to them. Then, they could all go together to splash in the Torres River and catch fish in the creeks, or slide barefooted on the black-green, slimy gutters in town, or enter the magic circle to play marbles with the chumicos. Equal to them. . .

Meanwhile, from the distance created by her patent-leather shoes, Anita observes the children's game. Among laughter and merriment, tic. . . tic. . . tic. . . The black chumicos of an infinite roundness, bumped each other within the circle until finally one knocked the other out of bounds. "Hooray, one down, only a few more left!" The chumicos chant promises of triumph.

From the depths of her pockets, Anita's marbles — shining colors, infinitely round, — do not chant promises of play games, but they look very pretty. Toc. . . Toc. . . Toc. . .in the bottom of her pocket Anita's marbles hopelessly knock against each other.

The church clock strikes five; time to stop the game and laughter; say "Goodbye, see you tomorrow," and end daydreams.

The children, so dirty, so tattered, joyously and noisily leave as they usually do. They rush to hungrily devour the thin soup made from bones reboiled, the plantain stew, and the stale tortillas. . .if they are lucky enough to have any left over from the day before.

Anita, always immaculate in her patent-leather shoes leaves like they do, only silently and sadly. With little appetite she sits down to eat the thick soup, and tender meat smothered with rich gravy. "And the penny-tree won't grow! Will it grow, Eufrasia, will it grow?" "If you water it with faith and love you'll see what a beautiful tree you'll have one of these days."

In the midst of all this, the chumico tree keeps on growing and filling the poor children's pockets with dreams and hopes. The ritual of the game — of life — is fulfilled again and again. . . but the penny-tree still does not grow.

Translated by Nuri Vallbona

PENELOPE'S SILVER WEDDING ANNIVERSARY

The party preparations have created an atmosphere of anxiety among us. One would think that we are about to entertain royalty. Maybe something exciting is finally about to happen in this weary town. Even I am extremely restless. I try to accommodate the day's vainly agitating hours into my quotidian work ritual but to no avail. Everything departs from habitual routines, escapes well defined limits to roll on towards the unexpected. And. . .Damn it! Would it really occur? What?

A party is a party, son-of-a-bitch. Relax those nerves. They are tightening up like violin strings. Don't let them quiver throughout your enormous body at the slightest clink of china that old Julia carefully handles.

"To think that I once held her in my arms when she was just a tiny little thing. Look at her now! I never would've believed that I could hold out for so many years. It's just incredible!" Julia goes on whistling her litany between the black gaps of her few remaining teeth. She washes and washes while creating in the kitchen sink an orchestration of porcelain, crystal, silverware and running water.

An unbearable garlic and fried-food odor not only impregnates the atmosphere but my insides as well, turning my stomach. I really **can't** tell if it's from the sickening smells or from what is about to occur tonight.

The noises, the cooking odors, mixed in with the piercing aroma of jasmines, roses, and gardenias, spinning a ball of nausea in my stomach almost contemptuously open distances between myself and things I normally manipulate with ease. It's as if these things are sacred and I am desecrating them. When I picked up the teaspoon, I dropped it superstitiously. Goddam this nausea! The cigarette I am lighting seems alive in my mouth. I let it fall without any desire of picking it up.

In the next room, María and Laura are singing while making their beds. Imaginary sailboats form in the air as they flap the fresh clean sheets, whose whiteness dazzles in the sunlight. As I lay unraveled on the couch, their youthful arms infused desires in me to enter their intimate circle of laughter, songs and kisses.

"They're your cousins, Louis, your orphaned cousins, whom you must love and respect always. You're evil, Louis! What you've done can cost you the tortures of hell. You must go to confession and never sin with them again!"

How soft and tender was their skin in the river waters! Never again did I experience such a complete and total paradise: The motley vegetation falling into the water in a transcendental suicide of branches thickened with parasites, bulrushes and lianes. The silence already perforated by a thousand noises, burst into a locust's soft whir, or into the plop of a ripe peach striking the earth, or into the flow of the river, or into the rush of blood laden with newly discovered pleasures — sound pleasures.

"You'll be damned in Hell! That's a mortal sin!"

Ah, but it was paradise, momma, the very same which I had magically sprouted at fourteen. That taste of moist virginal flesh which allowed me to delightfully bite it like a fresh, crisp apple!

Swollen with pleasures, their pubescent bodies would agitate in the river waters. I would close my eyes and let myself go. . .let myself go. . .let myself go. . . They would allow me to penetrate in the boundaries of their sensuous arms and legs that wrapped around my body like a fleshy net. There, I surrendered myself to the magic of relief after the long nights spent trying to calm the hard pain, that shameful pain in my groin.

Surrendering was paradise. Hell was those endless nights of hardened pain and fear of having to endure the swelling sin. That is Hell.

But momma — such a good woman, poor thing — was unable to understand then or now that games, bicycles, marbles, desks, books, and multiplication tables aren't everything.

There she sits knitting on the sofa next to the window — waiting for something? Knitting, always knitting. I know she is waiting for something. Every quick, nervous movement of her needle reveals that she is waiting. She's been waiting for so long! What had she knitted during that long stretch of time? She must have collected a roomful of bedspreads, pillows, sweaters, booties, hats, scarves. Where is she putting them all?

Today, with the bustle and preparation for the party — damned party that has me in this state — I think about momma's knitting with a strange uneasiness. Funny, where could she keep all those articles if she has never worn them or given them away? Could there be a secret room somewhere in the house? Where? White yarn, always pure white yarn.

Ever since my childhood, I have watched her knitting by the window while humming a melancholic waltz tune. Later, she would cover me with kisses that were marred by anxiety.

"Why do you knit so, momma?"

She would continue humming even though a teardrop would trickle down her cheek everytime I asked her.

"Where's that white sweater you knitted last week?"

Silently, she would rise up from the sofa to see if Julia had dinner ready or had prepared the biscuits. I have always asked her about it but I have never thought about momma and her knitting as I do today. Even from the very first moment that I listened to her speak and was able to understand her words, the only significant thing she uttered was "Sinner! You'll be damned in Hell! You're evil." Then, as if she had never entered into the magic circle of pleasurable laden flesh, she would go on muttering her household words: "sausage, potatoes, beans, laundry, roses, knitting. I must knit, I must finish these booties." When she says "I must" a gravestone situates itself over her body, burying everything alive while she prepares the soup or kneads the dough.

116

However, when she listens to a love ballad or the canary's warble, something suddenly trembles or seems to stir within her — something which reminds me of my cousins' magic circle. . . as if the doors to an unexpected paradise have opened within her. But, she continues talking about the same old things as if life were routine and a household chore. Dad impassively accepts her chatter. It isn't chatter. No. She strings words together which seem like chatter but really aren't. The funny thing is that each one of her words sounds as if she were carrying the thing she mentions in her mouth.

"Leave her be in her own world, Louis, she's happy there, in her simple feminine world. Twenty five years of marriage and not one complaint, not even a reproach. She's only content knitting, cooking, arranging floral bouquets, moving the furniture around. If our manly world were like theirs, everything would be a bed of roses. Look, look at these grey hairs — all from bending over a desk the whole day."

Momma doesn't have a single grey hair, but her eyes reveal the gravestone she carries, which entombs her life inside. In the mornings when she awakes, her complexion appears moist as if the early dew has watered the slight wrinkles that started to form around her eyes. Not a single grey hair. Always clean, shining, reddish-brown hair worn in an elegant bun. As long as she doesn't talk about household things ("bring the potato salad, Julia") one would think of her as an enchanting figure from a painting in a museum. When enunciating those household words in her homely voice, ("the stew is delicious today") her skin turns into vile, despicable material. One wants to muzzle her, hide her in the corner and plug one's ears to block out that dreadful sound, yet continue to gaze at her beauty and elegance. Why the hell doesn't she get away from her bananas, cabbage and vegetables. Oh momma, momma! How many embarassing moments have I experienced in front of my friends when she starts with the "the tomatoes are rotting. Aren't these green beans tender!" They look at me and shrug their shoulders, unable to understand her simple world. Then, they resume the conversation about everything that makes her cringe.

Today the party? For Chrissake! Why does it bug me so.? One more party like any other. The nausea remains stuck in my throat. Could any more knitted articles fit in momma's knitting room? Is she going to remain by the window? White yarn, white yarn, white yarn. . .

"Oh, those nights at the opera in the Music Hall. . .to be absorbed by the splendor of the chandeliers! To dance every night until the shoes wear out." When had she said all this? No, she never said it. I dreamed it in one of those childhood fantasies which are easily mistaken with reality.

"And the girls were always jealous of my dancing card. Everyone wanted to dance with me." What a vague sensation of having heard it coming from her lips. Maybe it hadn't been her. Someone had said it. Probably one of those vain old bags who always came to visit and to talk your ears off. White yarn, kitchen — nausea, nausea — it is her same old minute world which she would never leave. Poor thing. Just like grandmother and all the other women lacking wings to fly away to endless horizons, lacking dreams to conquer. . . Oh hell, what shitty thoughts. Everything's so dumb, the knitting room, the tiny fragile woman, who because of the emptiness within her, is a shadow. . . What the hell am I thinking about!

Warm, vibrant was María's flesh as her body trembled against my muscles, but she slipped away from me like a live fish. Beating ardently, she felt so tender pressed against me, while protecting her perverted virginity.

"You'll suffer in hell! You're evil!" Momma had said that, because she could not understand what ran through María when she rubbed her skin against mine and we reached for the ultimate. Momma didn't know anything about that. Had she ever experienced it, sometime with dad — with anyone? Impossible, she is indifferent, living only for white yarn and the kitchen. Strange, though, when the history professor lectured on the Trujillo's dictatorship, their orgies, and passions, momma had been present there, in my imagination, only she had seemed brisk, smiling. Her hair tumbled down in locks, while her dress had a provocative neckline. "And Trujillo wanted to seduce me, but I. . ." How absurd! She was not that old and besides, she is my mother who only knows how to say. . .

*****

The party finally started. The guests arrived. Little by little their fakery, lies and gossips, started to solidify in the spaces between their bodies. Laughter, hugs, kisses, — all had lost their essence and sincerity. I passed the time burdened by nausea and fear that momma would begin to fill her mouth with "bananas, tomatoes, stew, pies." How beautiful she looked, dressed in black which accented the reddishness of her hair. Imperial like never before. If only she could remain silent. . . If only she would remain aloof from every domestic article.

What? What in the hell are they saying? She's going to make an announcement? Everyone turned to look at her. Dad was shocked. This had to be a nightmare. She had never spoken in public. With all these vultures around ready to devour anyone alive, how could she dare make a fool out of herself? "Momma, for heaven's sake! Why the hell did you take that damn drink? You can't handle it. Liquor bewilders you. Come with me, momma."

"No. I want to tell my friends something very important. Leave me alone, Louis, and tell your father that I haven't even touched a drink."

"Momma, please, for your own good, be quiet."

Majestically, she raised herself on a platform and with authority managed to silence everyone. She had the most marvelous, royal aire about her. If only she could remain like that forever without saying. . .

118

"My very dear friends, especially you who have known us during our twenty-five years of marriage. I would like to be frank with you for the first time. How could I celebrate our silver wedding anniversary without sharing **my** happiness with you?" (Did she say **my** happiness like that, emphasizing **my**? And dad's? She's drunk. She's just not used to champagne. She's gone nuts.)

"Do you know what twenty five years of my life have been like with a cruel, selfish, stubborn, lustful man? I'm fed up." (Goddam! She's crazy, the champagne. . .her chatter!)

"Do you know how many sleepless nights and exhausting days of work I've lived through by his side?" (Shit, this is hell! A nightmare! She can't be saying this. She never knew how to express herself. She's drunk. Get her out of here.)

"No, I'm not going to recount every tear I've shed during the past twenty-five years. Why do you murmur among yourselves? I'm only going to tell you why I'm so happy. Why am I celebrating these twenty-five years? Well, I'll tell you: Louis is a man now and no longer needs me. As for my husband. . .What I'm celebrating today is my freedom. Have you ever seen a prisoner who has completed his sentence? Well, I'm that prisoner" (I can't take any more. The house is tumbling down on me.)

"Today I want to declare my independence from the yoke of marriage. As of now I'm free to dispose of my time as I please. No more measly trips to Galveston or Freeport where he'd take me while later he'd take his mistresses to Acapulco, Capri, and Biarritz. I'm going to travel around the world." (She's crazy, crazy, crazy!)

"The best thing about today is breaking that twenty-five year silence that has been eating me alive. Drink up my friends to the freedom that I now choose along with my ex-husband." (Dad, poor dad, how embarassing!)

"Right, dear? Isn't it a relief that I said it and not you? This way I'm the one who creates the scandal while you remain respectable in everyone's eyes. Just like always. Let's drink merrily, without animosity or hatred, happily like the good friends we've always been."

The sensation of the unreal atmosphere which chased me since morning overtook me with such force that I thought I had fallen victim to the many martinis I had drunk. I continued having the strangest impression that there were sacred distances between objects and myself. Those material objects which I had once touched without feeling, disappeared from my sight. They resisted touch, slipped away into nothingness and vanished in a horrendous nightmare.

Momma was still on the platform talking when I noticed that her beautiful black dress had a very provocative neckline. Her neck — I've never looked at it that way — was firm and fresh like María's and still exciting. . . For Chrissake, what am I thinking! She's my mother. There she stood laughing. . .laughing. . .laughing with that man, who was attractively grey.

Lustingly they gazed at each other with deep penetrating glances. I couldn't begin to imagine what they were telling each other. The martinis. . . I'm drunk. Momma, dad, twenty five years, the anniversary, that man Dr. Manzione, yes, it was Dr. Manzione, the one who saw her during her long illness. He saved her from death. . . now he was saving her from. . . Hell. . . evil. . . She's wicked like all the other women. . . They're exchanging glances. . . and dad? It's all the martinis' fault. I don't even know who I am.

She can't. She shouldn't break the monotonous ritual of the salads, breads, soups. . . Hell! Let her go on knitting by the window. I'll buy her all the white yarn she wants so she'll sew up that sinful neckline and stop looking at Dr. Manzione that way. She was born for knitting.

"There's still the rest of my life left to enjoy my own pleasure. Why not now while there's still time? Slavery is a thing of the past." (Damned to Hell. She's evil. She gazes at Dr. Manzione like María gazes at me when our flesh is saturated with each other. She too, condemned to hell. My pure mother is never tired of knitting futilities. Hell is the torture I'm going through today, not the river, or María's arms. I thought that. . .)

Everything became even more unreal when she brought out her knitted articles (white yarn, white, white everywhere!) and started passing them out among the guests. What resulted was unforeseen: everyone let themselves be carried away by her rapture and started putting on the articles they were given until they were crazily disguised by white wool, white, white, white wool. . . . They grew and grew among all that wool and under the bright lights, everyone fused into a white mass of arms and legs that shrieked with utmost confusion of liberty and lust.

Translated by Nuri Vallbona

PARABLE OF THE IMPOSSIBLE EDEN

She heard it for the first time during trivial chats with her friends, but she could not believe it. It was really as if she had never heard it at all, because what they told her failed to even scrape the outer crust of her soul. Later, her friends continued to discuss it. The ones who talked about it wore a deep blue star in their right eye. It was not the words, no, it was that star that suddenly aroused her soul, which had been deadened by her mechanical, domestic routine. She had converted that routine into a sacred ritual, a net woven meticulously to swathe and protect her from everything — everything that was not the present, the dustings, floor sweepings, diaper changings, dishwashings, husband-in-bed, and end-of-the-day emptiness that swirled within her. For many years, she had felt that her springs had gone limp, lifeless, like toys that are not real toys anymore having lost screws, bolts, strings, and pieces, but remain there, among the other toys that continue playing the game.

When she finally listened with her heart and discovered the deep blue star in the right eyes of the initiated few, she understood for the first time that her world of daily chores was an inferno where she had existed solely by conforming.

She had been buried alive for years, centuries, milliniums, fulfilling the housekeeping duties of Sisyphus. She wanted to escape.

One day she had made a superhuman effort to break open the cage of her monotonous inferno, but the attempt had been futile. She had then felt herself to be a prisoner more than ever before. Exhausted, she had receded into her cage where she remained still, gazing at everything from her dark inferno-without-star.

From there, she listened to the others, the real women. They could die with a smile on their face because they had experienced the paradise. She, however, would die compressed in her daily ritual, wearing a grimace of sickening emptiness.

Some time ago, a few women had left the paradise. One could tell by the wrinkles around their eyes and by their sagging breasts. But the glowing embers of the blue star, shining from the depths of their eyes, revealed that once they had been real women, not a half sketched shape like her.

She guessed that to reach the dreamy paradise, one must cross an endless sea in a vessel of rose petals. She began to build the vessel, carefully scrutinizing the first board, the first nail. She chose the size, shape, and color. Hopeless! Nails, boards, roses — they were only a black heap that would never mold the vessel which would take her to the paradise.

Those with the star in the right eye continued to whet her appetite for the bountiful paradise. Her resignation started to keep her from conforming to the rite of Sisyphus and she began to wander away from her small, compressed world to laze in dreamier regions. She sailed through seas of gold and silver, to fruitful isles where cascades echoed the whispers of love, and nude pure bodies surrendered to pleasures she had never known. Entering the sphere of pleasures, she savored paradise's ecstasy. But it was always a dream and her soul would awaken succumbed, desiring that blissfulness, craving it more and more each day.

When she finally built the vessel of fresh rose petals — was that also in a dream? — it sank in the middle of the sea, leaving only a few concentric circles and the anguish of having to swim to shore. It meant returning to the rite of Sisyphus to continue feeling empty and incomplete.

Several men came to her rescue, men without faces or names. When she saw them, she knew that they would melt away before reaching her, which in fact, they did. Actually, they disintegrated like old, decrepit things do, when they come in contact with fresh air.

Then he appeared — all muscular, handsome — and gave her his hand at that boring party of petty conversations that only serve to widen the distances between people. She knew that he would be the only one who could build the vessel, hoist the sails, head for the fruitful paradise and reach it. He began building the ship, and while its size grew, so did her impatience. She would raise her eyes to the skies in search for the blue star that was soon to come rest in her eye. Throughout her arid, rocky body covered with thorns, the seeds of anticipated pleasure began to stir.

One day, right in the middle of her daily rite, she forgot her role necessary for the reality of her home life to drag on and on as usual. Another day when she woke up, she did not even remember that she was the priestess of a ceremony, vital to the function of her home's machinery. And much later, while living in the future paradise, she completely forgot her daily inferno. It then became easy to hoist the sails, with his hand in hers, trembling of anticipated pleasure.

Oh, the splendid vision of fresh greenery — a new world! She entered triumphantly, gracefully, as if she had just come straight from the fine hands of the Maker. She carried a vague memory, more like a dream that had once happened just like this, but it was so blurred, so lost, in the milliniums of her being, that it was only a sensation.

She felt the overpowering voice that repeatedly said no. Her life had dragged a series of "no, you mustn't, no, no, no, no..." Because of that, she entered the paradise thinking only of that blue star. There, he gave her the flower of ecstacy, and in the luxury of the green grass between caresses, kisses and love, he set her on fire and impregnated her with the blue star light. Lavishly, he poured out an over abundance of pleasures; she scooped them up like an open glass. For the first time she felt whole. She felt like a real woman.

The first day, she discovered the delight of the sun, the grass, the birds, the creeks, the orchids and the mosses as if she had never experienced them before. The second day, the marvel of it all continued and then she was certain of bearing the blue star in her eye.

Nevertheless, the days, the weeks, the months, the spring, the summer, the fall and the winter recurred as on the other side of the paradise. The words, the caresses, the love, and everything, absolutely everything, began taking the shape of a rite. Again, not knowing when nor how, she began receding more painfully into her infernal cage, while gazing longingly at the shore that once she had abandoned full of hopes.

Translated by Nuri Vallbona

Three Short Stories By Rima Vallbona

Alicia G. R. Aldaya
Translated by
Eduardo C. Bejar

"Chumico Tree," "Penelope's Silver Wedding Anniversary," and "Parable of the Impossible Eden" constitute three recent contributions of Rima Vallbona to the Hispanic narrative.

The "Chumico Tree" belongs to the best tradition of literary realism. Behind its apparent simplicity, resulting from a carefully veiled technical command, the reader is confronted with a harsh reality and a poetic imbuement in adequate and corresponding proportions. This short story is an existential snapshot. Parallelism is its structuring principle. The omniscient narrator, by moving along the various locations where the action takes place, (the shabby school, under the chumico tree, at the noisy homes of the poor children, by the stakes designating the useless hope of the rich little girl or at his own silent house) is able to capture the unsolvable differences that exist between the world of the little rich girl Anita and that of the poor boy Chalo.

This radical and tragic dichotomy is repeatedly stated throughout the story. The poor children see her "through the pride of their barefeet and their mended uniforms." She in turn watches them, longing to participate in their games but her patchless uniform, patent-leather shoes, and "small white clean hands" draw her apart. Even the round chumico seeds sing promising songs of success for the poor children. Whereas Anita's marbles sing neither promises nor triumphs. While the majority of the children rush home to "hungrily devour the thin soup made from bones reboiled," Anita "with little appetite [...] sits down to eat the thick soup." In realistic and symbolic contrast, the chumico tree goes on growing but the penny-tree planted by the girl is doomed not to sprout.

Short dialogues indicate a social reality and define psychological characters. There is a sharp contrast between the crude language of Chalo with the kind begging words of Anita: "That's for you, meat-head!", said Chalo, "Have your rich daddy buy the chumicos with his móney." "Chalo, Chalito", said Anita, "be good like your mother, will you give me a chumico?" Between these different worlds language fails to serve as a bridge. The rhythmic and euphonic language of the narrator is successfully accomplished: "The boy opens the ritual by drawing the magic circle in the dust. Each hour turns into a whiff of time, a triumphant cry, a wild enjoyment."

Time and space have become inseparable; the insistence upon the hour acquires meaningful and revealing dimensions, which denote a probing concern on the infinity of time's limitlessness and hours constantly devoured by clocks and almanacs.

The circle in different forms is intentionally used as a symbol that elucidates the meaning of the "magical and the ritual" games of life. This time is not only used in the sense of the eternal return as interpreted by Azorín, but suggests a harmful lack of social mobility and negation of potential changes which would lead to a truly human solidarity.

A significant asset of this short story is the implicit impartiality of the narrator. On one hand, the "chumico tree" --universal symbol of the tree -- thrusts itself from earth to sky announcing its exuberant vegetal existence which bears many fruits, joys and compensations for the poor ones on Earth. On the other hand, there is Anita, the rich little girl, with her clean little hands as an innocent figure not to be blamed for the needs of the other children. Anita hopes that the future coins of her wishful tree will buy her their acceptance. This is an extreme paradox since the money which allows her to have new school uniforms and patent-leather shoes is precisely the barrier that keeps her isolated from her peers. It is a recurrent idea in the work of Rima Vallbona that money is not the "powerful knight" so well satirized by Quevedo. Neither money nor innocence, hope or the wish for solidarity will alter in the course of life these facts. This child-like microcosm so poetically and harshly depicted is part of a reality that implacably divides and isolates, sets promises and cruelly deceives.

"Penelope's Silver Wedding Anniversary" and "Parable of the Impossible Eden" are exponents of the life of the middle class bourgeoisie focusing on the role of woman in it; her oppressed acts of rebellion, the inadequate attempt of escaping from a meaningless life and her final failure. Generation after generation the Spanish woman has been conditioned to fit into a limiting mold assigned to her by society. If she succeeds in escaping from it, as she often does by means of idealized reality-distorting fantasies, she is incapable of accepting and adapting herself to the true fullness of life.

These two stories, realistic in nature and looking at society from a pessimistic viewpoint, are structured around multivalent symbols. In "Penelope," we find two contrasting levels and a constant interplay between form and content. The narrator is a young man who reveals to the reader, through his isolated thoughts, the logic and feelings of his masculine condition. With obvious inconsistency, he reproaches his mother's insipid conversation over superfluous domestic details. But,when she seems to have fulfilled all of her duties and demands placed upon her, the young man wants to keep her in the same dull and passive domestic world. For him, paradise is to be found in the pleasures of his young sensuality, all of them permissible, but to the woman mother, this aspect of human reality is forbidden. Her role as stated by the father, is "knitting, cooking, arranging floral bouquets, moving the furniture around." To execute the easy chores of the woman's world and her domestic duties should be sufficient to give meaning and a sense of purpose to her existence.

Over the centuries, this chauvinistic point of view has prevailed in Spanish society, placing a heavy burden on its women as it allows men to share their lives between home and the lover in turn. "Penelope" constitutes another denouncement of this pharisaical society that keeps women in this stiffling and submissive role.

The stream of consciousness of the narrator becomes the most important element of the story. The insistence upon his annoying nausea has in its reiteration a specific existential character. The statement "everything departs from habitual routines" is not limited only to the preparation for the festivity but a premonition that a radical and truly unexpected change is about to take place. Among the various elements of the two opposing planes of the story, the use of the alternating images is worth mentioning: the young, energetic, indiscriminate sensuality of the son, and the pale tediousness of maternal routine. This antagonistic duality highlights the narrative and underlines the reciprocal play between form and content. The river scenes are extremely poetic and vivid as a delicate reflection of another kind of relationship more real and human. The white colorless wool deprived of any shade used as a symbol of a routinary and monotonous life, is the key-motif of the story. The endless knitting stands for the relief and the necessary antidote to the suffocating simplicity of the feminine world. Sometimes wool is associated with the feminine world or with the subtle signs of an inner life that has been ill-treated and mutilated: ". . .she would cover me with kisses that were marred by anxiety." Other times, it becomes the grave stone that has kept her separated from her own deepest being. This time Penelope is the weaver of a shroud of unrealized dreams "never tired of knitting futilities."

Her prolonged passivity comes to a stop through the catalytic effects of a long illness and the influence of the family doctor who generates in her strong and vehement feelings towards the enjoyment of life. As the story ends during the festivities, an emotional chain reaction takes place. The "white" mass of guests starts indulging in the sensual pleasures and begins experiencing the newly found freedom of the mother as a final synthesis of all the contrasting elements present throughout the story.

There are reminiscences of "Penelope" in the subsequent story "Parable of the Impossible Eden." The main characters of both stories are condemned to a life of deadly domestic routines. In both, Paradise and Hell are present. The first one described in terms of exuberant, healthy sensuality and physical fulfillment; the light of the blue star conveying a subtle spiritual nuance. Hell is darkness, prison, routine, the repetitive execution of daily chores which do not enhance our spiritual growth; a mirror of the useless and painful Sisyphian rite.

The impact of "Parable of the Impossible Eden," implicit in its title, is achieved by the use of the traditional image of the voyage as evasion and adventure superseded at the end by the completion of the cycle of the unavoidable return of all things to their beginnings; philosophical concept that pervades all of Rima Vallbona's work.

It seems that we are reminded once more of the fugacity of paradisiacal ecstasy, or worse yet, that Paradise's fulfillment is unreachable. This metaphysical anguish however, does not remain with the reader. Instead, it remains the vague feeling of an idealized longing and the sentiment of nostalgia that stays with us when a dream, once it is accomplished, ceases to be a dream.

Notes On The Collaborators

ALICIA ALDAYA - Born in Havana, Cuba; Ph.D. Havana University, M.A. in English, Tulane University; is Associate Professor at the University of New Orleans. She has presented numerous papers to the SCMLA and has several publications in **Diario de las Américas, Poesía Hispánica, Letras Femeninas** and others.

EDUARDO C. BEJAR - Born in Havana, Cuba; B. Architecture, Rice University, 1966; Master in Spanish Literature, University of Houston, where he holds a lecturer's position in the Spanish Department. He practices Architecture for James A. Sink Associates in Houston.

CATHERINE G. BELLVER - Ph.D., M.A. University of California, Berkeley; B.A. Northwestern University; now teaching at the University of Nevada, Las Vegas. Publications: "Juan José Domenchina, Poet of Exile", "El Infierno de Angeles de Rafael Alberti". Many other works about Alberti have been published in **Hispanófila, KRQ, Cuadernos Hispanoamericanos** and **Revista de Estudios Hispánicos.** Among her honors: Phi Beta Kappa, Summa cum laude, Fulbright to Spain.

ELIZABETH ESPADAS - Ph.D. University of Illinois, M.A. New York University; is now Assistant Professor at the University of Delaware. She has published many articles in the **Journal of Spanish Studies: Twentieth Century; Books Abroad; Addendum; Papeles de Son Armadans, Spain; Hispanófila,** Cuadernos **Hispanoamericanos,** and others. Translator of short stories for a forthcoming book by Victoria Urbano. She is a member of the Editorial Board of **Letras Femeninas.**

KATHLEEN M. GLENN - Ph.D., Stanford University, California. Associate Professor of Spanish, Wake Forest University, Winston Salem, N.C. Her publications include **The Novelistic Technique of Azorín,** many articles on the post-Civil War novel of Spain, an Interview of Victoria Urbano, and many other studies. She is a member of the Editorial Board of the **Journal of Spanish Studies: Twentieth Century;** Associate Editor of **Anales de la novela de postguerra,** and Editor (1977-78) of **Letras Femeninas.**

VIVIAN GRUBER - Ph.D., M.A., B.A. Florida State University. Now teaching at Stephen F. Austin State University. Her publications include: "Development in the Poetry of Gabriela Mistral"; "Cantigas de Alfonso el Sabio"; "A Search for Identity: The Adolescent in the Latin American Novel" and many other articles. Honors: Fulbright Research Fellowship for France, 1964. Scholarship, American Association of University Women, 1947-1948. She is a Member of the Editorial Board of **Letras Femeninas;** member of the Bilingual Education Committee, and many others.

MARY SUE LISTERMAN - Ph.D. University of Missouri; M.A. Middlebury College; B.A. Southern Methodist University. Now teaching at Miami University, Ohio. Her publications include: **Angel María de Lera,** Twaine World Publishing Co.; several studies about Juan Ramón Jiménez, and about the **Spanish Civil War Trilogy** by Angel María de Lera.

CORINA S. MATHIEU - Born in Buenos Aires, Argentina, Ph.D. Stanford University; now teaching at the University of Nevada, Las Vegas. Her publications include numerous articles in **Hispanófila, Latin American Review, Nueva Narrativa Hispanoamericana, Handbook of Latin American Studies,** and **Letras Femeninas.**

ROBERTO OLIVERA - Born in Córdoba, Argentina, he is a graduate of Middlebury College and is now working towards his Ph.D. His publications include: **Agonías sin lugar; Al borde de otras pieles** (poetry); **Las últimas horas para Norma** (play), and **Dioses y juguetes** (short sketches and monologues).

MARTHA ONAN - Ph.D., Professor and Chairman of Foreign Languages State University of New York, Brockport, N.Y. She is Editor of **Twentieth Century Foreign Women Writers** and Chairman of the Committee of **FOLIO,** a publication devoted to the study of foreign languages and literature. She has translated several chapters from Victoria Urbano's book about Yolanda Oreamuno. She has many publications and honors.

MARIE J. PANICO - Ph.D., is presently teaching Spanish at Fairfield University, Fairfield, Connecticut. Her publications include many scholarly articles. She has done extensive research on the works of Octavio Paz, one of which, "Erotismo y trascendencia en Ocatavio Paz" was presented at the Fall Meeting of the Asociación de Literatura Femenina Hispánica in 1976. She has lectured in Puerto Rico, New York and at the Department of Commerce in Washington; was Editor of the Archive of Hispanic Literature and Consultant for the Hispanic Foundation of the Library of Congress. She is presently translating a novel.

KATHERINE C. RICHARDS - Born in Tuscaloosa, Alabama, she received degrees in Spanish from the University of Alabama (B.A. 1962) and Tulane University (M.A. 1969), and (Ph.D. 1971). Her honors include membership in Phi Beta Kappa, NDEA Fellowship and a teaching assistantship at Tulane University, then she received a Research Grant from the College of Liberal Arts of Texas A&M University. She has read papers for many professional associations. Her publications include many articles about Miguel de Unamuno, and the Guatemalan dramatist, Carlos Solórzano.

ARNEY L. STRICKLAND - is Associate Professor of English and Head of the English Department at Lamar University, Beaumont, Texas. He has studied the Spanish language and literature with Professor Victoria Urbano. He took his doctorate in English and English Education at Ball State University, Muncie, Indiana. Many of his publications have appeared in **Southwestern American Literature, The Western Carolina Journal of Education,** and the **Newsletter of the American Dialect Society.**

PAT HOLLIS SMITH - M.A. candidate Educational Diagnostician, Lamar University 1978; Research Assistant to Dr. Victoria Urbano 1974-75; Arrangements Editor **Freeway to Italian** 1976-77; Secretary of Asociación de Literatura Femenina Hispánica 1977-78 and Board Member of the same; Teaching Fellow, Department of Modern Languages, Lamar University, 1978, Assistant Editor of **FIVE WOMEN WRITERS OF COSTA RICA,** 1978. Her publications include Spanish Poetry in English translation; Review on Julia Maura's play **Doña Juana;** studies on Valle Inclán's **La rosa de papel,** and García Lorca's **Don Perlimplín.**

VICTORIA E. URBANO - Ph.D. Magna Cum Laude and M.A. University of Madrid, Spain; Drama, Royal Conservatory of Dramatic Arts, Madrid; Journalism, Panamerican School of New York. Professor of Modern Languages (Spanish and Italian) Lamar University. In 1972 was awarded the title for life of Regents' Professor in recognition of distinguished teaching and research. She has traveled and lectured extensively throughout Europe and America. Author of many books (see biographical notes, page 110) she has also published some textbooks including **Freeway to Italian** 1977 used by Lamar-Rome Program. She is Founder and Director of Asociación de Literatura Hispánica and of its journal **Letras Femeninas.** Recipient of many international awards and honors, she is Vice Consul of Costa Rica in Houston and Beaumont, Texas, serves as Consultant in the field of Spanish and Latin American theater and literature, and is Editor of **FIVE WOMEN WRITERS OF COSTA RICA.**

NURIA VALLBONA - Oldest child of Rima Vallbona, born in Houston in 1957. She graduated from Duchesne Academy with the highest honors and a Special Award in Journalism. She is presently studying Journalism at the University of Texas School of Communications. In collaboration with her mother, she has prepared in English a book of short stories **Mirror of Lineliness** forthcoming by Vantage Press.

RIMA VALLBONA - M.A. University of Costa Rica and is now working on her Ph.D. dissertation. She is Associate Professor at St. Thomas University, Houston, where previously served as Chairman of Spanish for several years. Author of many articles, short stories and novels (see biographical notes page 112) she is Chairman of the Editorial Council of **Letras Femeninas.**